Thundering Giants

The Laidlaw Reading Program LEVEL 10

William Eller
Kathleen B. Hester

S. Elizabeth Davis
Thomas J. Edwards
Roger Farr
Jack W. Humphrey
DayAnn McClenathan

Nancy Lee Roser
Elizabeth M. Ryan
Ann Myra Seaver
Marian Alice Simmons
Margaret Wittrig

Patricia J. Cianciolo, *Children's literature*
David W. Reed, *Linguistics*

LAIDLAW BROTHERS • PUBLISHERS
A Division of Doubleday & Company, Inc.

RIVER FOREST, ILLINOIS

Irvine, California   Chamblee, Georgia   Dallas, Texas   Toronto, Canada

Page

Tricked Again!

Just for Fun

Book-length Story

Wondering... Then Deciding

Kumi and the Pearl

Kumi stood on the quay at her grandfather's pearl farm, watching the diving girls. Momo, her very small sister, stirred against her back.

More than anything, Kumi wished that Momo would grow big enough to walk. Until Momo walked, Kumi could not be a diving girl and hunt for oysters in the sea.

She talked to her grandfather about it. "Please, Ojii-chan, when can I be a diving girl?"

"My youngest diver is but fourteen years old," Grandfather said. "You are young."

"I am almost eleven, Ojii-chan."

Grandfather shook his head. "When Momo can walk, I will teach you to dive as I taught you to swim. You have much to learn before you can dive for oysters. You will learn to hold your breath under water for the proper length of time. When Momo can walk, I will teach you. Until then you will care for your small sister."

Kumi sighed. This she must do for her family. All day her mother sewed, making kimonos for visitors who came to see the pearl farm. Her father and brothers worked in the sheds, helping Grandfather. There was no one else to care for Momo.

Today she looked for her friend Yukiko. But Yukiko was not in the sheds nor on the quay watching the girls. Kumi would watch alone. Alone, unless one counted Momo, sleeping against her back.

Now and then a shining face and dripping white-shirted shoulders pushed up through the water, and an arm emptied a net full of oysters into a tub.

There was the youngest diver, placing an oyster into a nearby tub! Proudly, the girl pushed a strand of hair into the knot at the back of her neck—the beautiful knot of shining hair that the diving girls wear. Thoughtfully, Kumi touched a strand of her own long hair.

Grandfather came along the quay, his clogs making a pleasant sound against the wood. He looked closely at an oyster basket swinging in the water. There it would hang safely for many years, waiting for the harvest of pearls. "Jewels of the sea," Grandfather said.

No one in all Japan was happier than a diving girl at harvest time. Perhaps Momo would walk soon—perhaps she would walk tonight, at home.

Kumi reached the door of her house. She took off her clogs and said politely, "I have returned."

Her mother looked up and smiled. Then she sewed the last tiny stitches in the sleeve of a red silk kimono.

Kumi unwrapped the scarf that held Momo. Carefully she set Momo on her feet and held her upright.

"Walk, Momo," she whispered. "Walk."

Kumi moved her hands away. Momo's fat legs folded, and she sat on the floor. "It is not yet the proper time," Kumi thought.

She piled coals on top of one another and started a fire. Then she waited for the coals to grow gray. Soon Grandfather and her father and brothers would come home ready for rice.

After rice Grandfather looked outside. "We will walk and enjoy the beauty that is here for those who will look," he said. "Tonight the Milky Way, River of Heaven, flows in the sky."

So Kumi, her mother, and Grandfather walked and saw the things that were beautiful. They saw the moon that shone like a thin pearl hanging on a string of stars. They saw the branches of trees that seemed to brush the sky.

Finally they came to the bank of a river, and they climbed a path beside it. On they went, around a curve where the river widened and quieted, on to a deep, small pool.

In the pool the stars of the River of Heaven shone like thousands of fireflies.

"It is here that I learned to dive," Kumi's mother said.

Grandfather nodded. "The pool is deep. It is almost as deep as the water at the farm."

Kumi touched her mother's sleeve. "When you were a small girl, how did you learn to stay under water?"

"Your grandfather taught me," her mother said. "He taught me as he will teach you, when the time comes. I remember well. I counted the seconds each time I slipped into the water. I measured them slowly, one count for each second of time, until there was one minute."

A Surprise for Ojii-chan

The next morning Kumi's father and brothers started for the farm. When they were gone, Kumi wound Momo against her back.

"Now we will see what the new day has brought," she said. "Who knows, we may find a kingfisher's nest of fish bones." She stepped into her clogs.

"I am going," she said.

She walked along the short street with its row of brown houses, on past the pearl farm, where she turned to climb the hill.

She followed beside the river, on and on, until she came to the quiet, deep pool.

Far below she could see the pearl farm and the sheds where girls worked.

Grandfather looked as small as a toy general. He walked along the quay, stopping now and then beside a bamboo float.

Kumi listened to the splash of river against rock, and she looked down into the clear pool of green water. The water would be cold—cold from the snows of the mountains.

Across the river, a great mountain rose against the blue-green of the sky.

She turned from the river and walked along the path until she came to a peach tree. Something stirred in the branches. And there was Yukiko sitting in the tree. Quickly she slid to the ground and reached for Momo.

"Let me carry her," she said.

"If you carry her, Yukiko, I will dive in the pool," Kumi said. "Then I will watch her while you dive."

"I will care for her," said Yukiko. "I don't like cold water in my ears."

So Kumi unwound the scarf that held Momo. Then, as Kumi undressed, Yukiko and Momo laughed together.

Kumi slipped into the water.

Down she went, forcing herself on, until she felt the stones against her feet. She bounced there like a ball and measured out the seconds. When she knew that she must take a breath, she kicked up to the surface.

Again and again she went to the bottom of the pool. Once a small fish almost touched her nose. Kumi rocked back and forth to keep from floating to the surface. She counted, one . . . two . . . three . . . and on to ten. Now up!

She climbed out and sat on a rock to dry.

Every morning Kumi and Momo met Yukiko at the peach tree. Each day Kumi would dive into the pool. Each day she would stay a few seconds longer while Momo and Yukiko played.

When they arrived at the pearl farm, Grandfather looked at them and smiled. "They are always together, those three," he said.

"They are friends," Yukiko's father said.

Then came the time when Kumi could stay under the water for almost a minute. "One more day. One more day," she thought to herself. "Perhaps tomorrow I will count to sixty."

Early the next morning she and Momo went up the hill again. Kumi looked up into the branches of the peach tree, but Yukiko was not there. Kumi waited a long time. "Yukiko isn't coming. What can I do with Momo?"

Kumi looked up at the peach tree. Its branches were safe and strong.

"Momo, the tree is like a mother. You shall swing here in the hammock of your scarf, safe as a peach on a tree."

She unwound the scarf, around and around, and folded it into a blue hammock that held Momo easily. She tied the ends to a branch in the tree, and Momo lay there, swinging back and forth. Soon her eyes shut, and she slept.

Kumi let herself down from the tree and slithered and slid to the river's edge. She dropped her kimono and kicked off her clogs.

Again and again she went into the water. She stayed under sixty seconds every time before coming to the surface! What a wonderful surprise this would be for Grandfather! She sat on the bank and hugged her knees.

Far below she saw Grandfather walking toward the path that led to the river.

Kumi quickly dressed and hurried to the tree. She did not want Grandfather to find her here. Then he would not be surprised. She untied the blue scarf. For a second it caught against a twig, and she tugged it free. Holding Momo close, she slipped to the ground.

She swiftly followed a path toward the row of houses. She walked past a field of rice, past rows of small fish hanging to dry in the sun, past a turnip field. Then she turned off the path and went toward the farm.

Only Yukiko's father was at the farm.

"Where is Yukiko today?" Kumi asked.

"She is helping her mother," he said. "Your grandfather is looking for you."

Then she heard her grandfather's voice.

"I saw you on the hillside," he said. "You walked alone." In his hand he held a bit of blue silk, the silk of the scarf that held Momo, the silk that had caught in the branches. His voice was quiet. "You made a hammock."

"Yes, Ojii-chan," Kumi whispered.

"You made a hammock, and you left Momo alone in the tree."

"Yes, Ojii-chan," said Kumi, her lips barely moving.

"You will not leave her again, Kumi," said Grandfather as he turned away.

A Moment to Decide

Sadly, Kumi walked with Momo, and the late afternoon grew dark and cloudy. She walked to the top of the hill. There the wind blew hard, almost as though a great storm might be coming from the sea at any moment.

Below, Grandfather worked alone on the quay.

The wind blew with fresh, angry force. Suddenly Kumi saw Grandfather slip into the water, his arms spread wide on the floats. He didn't move—he, who could swim better than anyone.

No one hurried to help him. No one was there to help—

She unwound the scarf and tied Momo close to a branch where she could not rock in the wind. Grandfather had said that she must not leave Momo, but surely, surely, this was a time not to listen. Momo would be safe, and Grandfather was in danger. She dropped to the ground and ran swiftly, pushing against the wind.

As her clogs creaked on the quay, she tried to call, but the words blew away in the wind.

"My foot is caught, and I cannot move it," Grandfather said.

Kumi kicked off her clogs and dropped into the cold water. Grandfather's foot was stuck between the pier and a bamboo pole. She tugged at the pole. For one minute she struggled to free his foot, and then she pushed to the surface to catch her breath.

"You cannot move the pier," Grandfather said. "You must go for help."

"There is only one bamboo pole to move—please." Kumi slipped down into the water. She held the pole with both hands and twisted her body as she tugged. The sixty seconds were almost over—the pole moved.

Again Kumi rose to the surface. She shook the water from her face. "Once more, Grandfather."

And with the next tug, Grandfather pulled himself from the water. He reached out his hand to Kumi. "How is it that you hold your breath under water?" he asked.

"I practiced at the deep pool," Kumi said.

"And Momo stayed in the peach tree?"

"Only one time. Yukiko cared for her."

"And now? Momo is in the tree?" Grandfather asked.

"Yes," Kumi said softly.

"I see," Grandfather said. "I see."

Grandfather swiftly led the way up the hill. Momo was still sleeping in her hammock. She awakened and cried when she was wrapped against Kumi's wet kimono.

The next night after rice, Grandfather reached for his pipe. "Tomorrow . . . I will have a new diver . . . a young diver . . . who is almost . . . eleven years old. I spoke to Yukiko's father. Yukiko wishes . . . to care for Momo until Momo can walk . . ."

Kumi threw her arms around her grandfather's neck. "How can I wait until tomorrow? How can I wait?"

The next morning she floated near her own wooden tub. A long rope that was tied around her reached to the tub. Deep under water she felt along the shoreline. Her fingers dragged over the bottom until she found an oyster. She twisted it free and kicked to the top.

"Swim here," Grandfather called. He reached for the oyster. "We will mark this one. When harvest time comes, the pearl will be yours to keep."

"Please, Ojii-chan, the pearl will be for Yukiko, who watches Momo."

"It shall be as you wish," Grandfather said.

That night Kumi and Grandfather walked in their garden.

Clouds edged with light floated across the moon.

Proudly, Kumi pushed a strand of hair into the small knot at the back of her neck—that knot of shining hair that the diving girls wear.

Call Me Pilar

"Pilar, will you come here for a minute?" called her father.

Pilar pretended she didn't hear. She carefully wiped off a knife and laid it in the sink. Then she wiped her hands on a towel.

"Pilar, did you hear me?" asked her father from the doorway.

The young girl turned around, her eyes flashing with anger. "Please, Papa!" she cried, dropping the towel. "Don't call me Pilar!"

"Why not?" her father asked in a surprised voice. "That is your name."

"But I don't want it to be my name," she replied. "Pilar is a Spanish name. I want to be called Polly."

"Polly?" asked Mr. Rios. "Pilar is as good a name as Polly!"

"Pilar is not a good name!" she cried. "Kids in the United States don't have funny names like Pilar. Everybody laughs when they hear it. So please call me Polly."

"I see," said Mr. Rios. His daughter's anger troubled him. Pilar had been unhappy about so many things since the family had moved from Mexico to the United States.

"And please don't talk in Spanish," she added. "Speak English so that my friends will understand what you're saying. They laugh when they hear you talk."

"Why do they laugh?" asked Mr. Rios.

"Because the language is different," she answered. "That's why."

"Is it bad to be different?" her father wanted to know.

"Yes, Papa," she cried. "It's very bad to be different. I want to be like my friends."

Mr. Rios shook his head.

"And another thing," continued Pilar. "It's bad enough that you speak a different language. But it's even worse that you go to school!"

"How else can I learn?" demanded Mr. Rios. "You want me to speak English, do you not? I go to school to learn how to speak good English."

"But you're too old to go to school. School is for kids."

"There are no children in my class—only big people," explained her father. "Our teacher does not think we are too old to be there. She is glad to help us. Is that wrong?"

By this time, Pilar wished she hadn't brought up the subject of school—or English—or even her name. So many things were hard to explain! She loved her family, but she couldn't accept the fact that they weren't like other people.

The following Wednesday Pilar brought a friend home from school. She had hoped they would be alone, but they found Mr. Rios working at the kitchen table.

"Joan and I have to do some math, Papa," said Pilar. "We need to use the table." Mr. Rios moved his papers out of their way.

"Now there is room for all of us," he said. "But we must work quietly, for your mother is still sick."

The girls sat down and started to do some math problems. After a moment Joan noticed an odd look on Mr. Rios' face. "Are we bothering you?" she asked.

"No," he said. "But I do not know this word. English is a hard subject for me."

"Maybe I can help," offered Joan.

Pilar gave her a cross look. "My father does not need your help," she said quietly.

"Pardon me, little one, but I do!" said Mr. Rios. And he held out his book, pointing to a word on the page.

"That word is *bubble,*" said Joan.

Mr. Rios laughed. "English is hard to read," he said. "That is why I go to school at night."

"By the way, Mr. Rios, are you coming to our school tonight?" asked Joan.

Mr. Rios looked surprised. "Why should I come to your school tonight?" he wanted to know.

"All the parents will be there," explained Joan. "Our school is having an open house so the parents can talk to the teachers. Didn't Polly tell you?"

Pilar caught her breath. She hadn't intended to tell her parents about the open house. She didn't look at her father when she said, "I—I guess I forgot to tell him."

Her father realized that she didn't want him to visit school. His daughter could not accept the fact that her family was different.

He turned to Joan and said, "Mrs. Rios has a bad cough. Maybe that is why Pilar did not tell me. I think it is good to meet Pilar's teacher, so I will try to be there."

Why had Pilar been unhappy since she had moved to the United States with her family?

Thank You, Amigo

That night as he was getting ready to leave the apartment, Mr. Rios told Pilar, "You do not need to go to the school with me. I do not mind if I go alone."

"Everybody will know you're my father," she replied. "So I might as well go, too."

Before long Pilar and her father arrived at the school. People were walking in and out of the classrooms, talking and laughing in a friendly way. Pilar led her father to her room and over to her teacher. "Mrs. Majors, I'd like you to meet my father," she said. "My mother has a bad cough and couldn't come tonight."

"Hello, Mr. Rios," replied Mrs. Majors. "I'm glad you could come." She looked at Pilar. "I'd be so grateful if you and your father would stay a minute after the others go home. I need your father's help."

Pilar thought it was odd that her teacher should ask such a thing. "But how can my father help you?" she burst out.

Mrs. Majors just smiled. "I'll tell you later. Now if you'll pardon me, I must speak to some other parents."

When everyone had left, Mrs. Majors explained her problem to Mr. Rios and Pilar. "I intend to take a vacation in Mexico next summer," she said. "So I have been going to class at night, trying to learn Spanish."

Then she laughed shyly and said, "But to tell the truth, you might describe me as a slow learner! I can't seem to catch on to the language. I imagine that you are busy, but I would be so grateful if you would help me."

Mr. Rios was too surprised to answer.

"Of course, I know I'll never be able to speak beautiful Spanish like you do," Mrs. Majors quickly added.

Pilar couldn't believe her ears. She had never heard anyone describe Spanish as a beautiful language.

"And you'll laugh at the way I speak," Mrs. Majors continued. "But with your help, maybe I will catch up with the others in my class."

Mr. Rios burst out laughing. "I will not laugh at your Spanish if you do not laugh at my English!"

"Thank you, amigo," Mrs. Majors said.

"Ah, I see you know the Spanish word for friend," he said. "It is a fine way to begin!"

As they left the building, Pilar finally spoke. "Just imagine!" she said. "My teacher goes to school. And she's as old as you are!"

When they reached the street, they saw Joan and her father. Joan turned around and called, "Where were you? I've been looking every place for you."

Joan turned to her father. "Dad, I'd like you to meet Mr. Rios and my friend, Polly."

The two men shook hands. Then Mr. Burns said, "I've heard a lot about you, Polly. I'm grateful to you for helping Joan with her math."

"That's OK," Pilar replied. "Math is one of my favorite subjects."

Mr. Rios put his arm around his daughter. "Pilar—I mean Polly—is very good in math," he boasted.

"Papa, you don't have to call me Polly," she said.

"But I thought you liked that name," replied Mr. Rios.

The girl smiled at her father. "From now on, just call me Pilar."

Scat!

Scat was his name. Everybody called him that because he was always getting into mischief. He always wanted to know what the grown-ups were talking about. And he did things he was told not to do. People got tired of telling him to keep out of mischief. Pretty soon they just said, "Scat, Jim. Scat!"

And that was how Scat got his name.

When he was nine years old, there was one thing Scat wanted more than anything else. He wanted to follow his father into town at night and listen to him play his shiny, brass trumpet. Scat's father was in a band and could play some of the sweetest music ever heard. There were other brass instruments, too. But none of the instruments sounded as good to Scat as the trumpet.

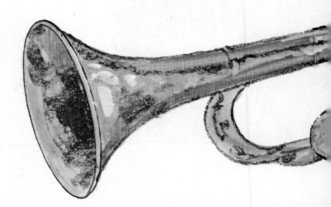

Some people called the music jazz, and some people called the music blues. Scat thought it didn't matter whether the music was called jazz or blues as long as people liked the way it sounded. He liked the music so much that it started his feet dancing and his arms moving.

His father never minded if Scat came along, just so he didn't get into mischief. His mother didn't mind, either. But one person did mind, and she minded a lot! That person was Scat's grandma.

Scat, his mother and father, his brother, and an uncle lived with Grandma. She was the head of the house. When she said something, she meant it. And when she laid down the law, it was really laid down. But even Grandma's laws weren't always obeyed.

"Listen to me, Charles Brown!" she said when she got mad at Scat's father. "No son of mine is going to play that awful music."

"But I'm going to," answered Scat's father, trying to defend himself. "Jazz sounds good."

"Why, it's not even music," Grandma argued. "It's just wild, good-for-nothing noise! That's all it is. A gentleman wouldn't have anything to do with that kind of low-down music."

"But I like jazz," replied Scat's father.

"That don't matter," argued Grandma. "Like it or not, jazz is no music for a gentleman."

Scat's father stopped trying to defend his playing. "I'm going to blow my trumpet, and nobody's going to stop me!"

"Well, play if you got to," Grandma finally said, "but don't take Scat along with you! You hear me?"

Scat intended to obey Grandma, but sometimes it wasn't easy. Some nights he would wait till she was resting or visiting neighbors. Then he'd slip into town to listen to his father's trumpet and the other brass instruments.

Scat wanted to make music himself. This made Grandma happy because she liked music, too. Church-going kind of music. She had a deep voice, and she tried to get Scat to sing along with her. But Scat didn't want to sing. He wanted to play an instrument.

"Isn't there anything I can learn to make music with?" he asked his father. "I just got to learn some instrument."

"Anybody that wants to make music makes it!" Scat's father said. "Why, some of the best music I ever heard was played on an old washboard or tin pan."

"Who wants to play on a tin pan?" cried Scat. "I want a real instrument!"

"Just wait till your birthday, Son," replied his father. "I'll get you something real good to make music on."

Scat thought that time had never passed so slowly as he waited for his birthday. First one week passed. And then another. And then still another. And then one night Scat's father came home with a little red box. In an instant Scat had the package opened. Inside was a harmonica!

Nobody had to teach Scat how to use the harmonica. He was mouthing it and playing it and touching it with different fingers all through the day. He learned by trying and trying, and trying some more.

Scat soon learned to make the harmonica growl and sing and play fast tunes that sounded very much like jazz. That was when Grandma said, "That's a funny kind of music. I'm not sure I like it at all!"

Although more and more people were beginning to like this new music called jazz, Grandma thought it was shameful. She went her own way and thought her own thoughts. "You listen to what your heart says," she told Scat. "Listen to what the little voice inside you keeps saying. That'll set you straight."

"What little voice?" asked Scat.

"You just listen. You'll hear it. Do what your heart tells you—not your head."

Scat thought it was mighty funny how often Grandma's heart told her to grumble about jazz. Then one morning he heard her say, "Why, just look at that!" She pointed toward the alley behind the house.

"Look at what?" Scat asked. But he knew very well what.

There were Scat's father and some other men who played in the jazz band marching down the alley. As they filed past the house, the music was loud and sweet.

Scat knew that Mr. Jackson had died and that this was the band's way of saying good-bye.

Jazz funerals always made Grandma grumble more than ever. She hated seeing Scat's father marching in the loud parades. There he was now, his brass trumpet blowing loud and strong. At that very instant Scat realized that jazz was a strange kind of music. It was sad and happy, all at the same time.

Grandma stared through the window and said, "One thing I know for sure—a jazz funeral is a no-good funeral. It's not for a gentleman."

As the men filed on down the alley, their music grew faint. Grandma shook her head and said, "Shameful, that's what it is."

When Scat's father got home, Grandma spoke her mind again. But Scat's father defended himself. "Bill Jackson loved jazz. I can't think of any better way of saying good-bye!"

"Not proper," she grumbled. "It's just not proper at all!"

When Scat was ten, his grandma became sick with a cough. She got better for a while, and then she started to cough harder than ever. She didn't grumble as much as she used to. And then she got very thin, and one day she died.

Scat cried—but not very much. He didn't know why—because he'd loved Grandma a lot. "Why, boy—there isn't so much to cry about," his father said. "Your grandma had a good, long life. She had a lot of sad times and a lot of happy times, too. And man—just look at all the children and grandchildren and great-grandchildren! You know, I think Grandma was weary. She was just weary and wanted to rest."

"I'll miss her," replied Scat in a faint voice.

Everybody in town went to Grandma's funeral. Everybody seemed sad, except Scat and his father. There were a lot of tears, and crying sounds, too. But after a while, all the people started to go away. And then the sun started to go down, and a fresh breeze started blowing through the treetops. Scat felt strange—sad and happy at the same time. Just the way a lot of jazz music sounded.

Scat looked at the leaves flashing and shining in the sun. He listened to the gentle wind whistling around the trees, lifting the branches and playing with the leaves. Everyone was gone now.

Scat wanted to say good-bye to Grandma in his own way. He couldn't help remembering how she hated jazz funerals, but she had told him to listen to his heart, not his head. She had wanted him to do whatever was proper.

So Scat took his harmonica out of his pocket and began to play.

Josefina February

Not long ago there lived a little girl named
Josefina February. Josefina lived with her
grandfather in a house that had one room, bamboo
walls, and a banana-leaf roof.

In front of their house stood a huge tree in which
Josefina had her very own sitting room. From her
room in the tree, she could watch the sea three miles
away and the marketplace, which was nearly
halfway to the sea.

In back of their house was a grove where oranges,
coconuts, bananas, and vegetables grew. Flowers
were everywhere, covering the ground and circling
the trunks of the calabash trees.

Early every morning Josefina and her grandfather went to the grove and picked the ripe fruit. They carried it in baskets on their head and walked down the hill to the marketplace. With the money they earned from the fruit they sold, they bought candles, beans, salt, and sometimes cloth. Mr. February always gave Josefina a penny or two to spend as she pleased.

53

Josefina loved the marketplace. There was so much to see and smell and hear. People, baskets, hats, and mats were all mixed together with heaps of coffee beans and rice. Meat and beans boiled in big, black kettles that hung over hot coals. There were sugarcane candies and heaps of coconuts to be sold. There were beads and shoes, calabash bowls and chairs everywhere. Church bells rang, and children blew bamboo trumpets.

One morning, instead of going to market, Mr. February planned to work in Mr. Hippolyte's sugarcane fields. "Stay at home today," he told Josefina. "We'll go to the market tomorrow." But Josefina had other plans.

Today was her grandfather's birthday, and she intended to buy him a pair of leather shoes—real leather shoes. So she decided to go to the market alone, hoping to sell one basket of fruit. Then she would have enough money, with the pennies she had saved, to buy the shoes.

After her grandfather left, Josefina took her basket and went to the grove. While she was picking the ripe fruit, she heard a faint sound. It seemed to come from the coffee berry bush. Josefina looked behind the bush and saw a little black burro. It had a mane of brown hair that looked like a cap. Its legs were so shaky it could hardly stand, and its ears looked as long as its legs.

Josefina picked it up and held it close, rubbing her hand over its mane. The little burro folded its soft ears and leaned its head against Josefina's chest. She decided to call it Cap.

She wondered if Cap belonged to someone. How she wished the little burro could be her playmate! She would play games with him, and when Cap was older, she would ride on his back to the sea.

Josefina was so busy dreaming that it was past noon before she remembered the fruit she had picked. She couldn't bear the thought of leaving Cap, so she decided to take him to the marketplace with her.

As she stood in the afternoon sun, Josefina suddenly felt cold. What if Cap belonged to the very first person she met? If Cap belonged to someone else, he couldn't belong to her!

But perhaps Cap was like Josefina and had no mother, no father, no sister, no brother. Cap might not even have a grandfather. He might, just possibly, belong to no one in the whole world!

Now she felt better—warmer, too. She hugged Cap tightly to her chest for a moment. Then she put him down, set her basket on her head, and started down the hill. The burro followed close at her heels.

The first person she met was Lilly, the tallest, proudest girl on the hill. Lilly had a basket full of ripe bananas on her head. "Pardon me, Lilly," Josefina said. "As you can see, I have a baby burro. Does he belong to you?"

Lilly gave Josefina an odd look and swept by without saying a word.

When Lilly had gone, Josefina whispered to Cap, "Well, anyway, you didn't belong to the first person."

She continued on, half walking, half skipping, until she reached the bottom of the hill. There she saw a little girl and her brother, who were selling coconuts by the roadside.

Josefina went up to them and said, "Pardon me. As you can see, I have a baby burro. What do you think of him?"

"I wish he belonged to me!" replied the girl.

"A burro would make a great playmate!" remarked her brother.

A feeling of happiness swept over Josefina. So far Cap belonged to no one. She skipped along happily, the burro still close at her heels.

Soon she came to a house that looked like a kite on a string. It belonged to two sisters who were twins. The sisters, named Yvette and Yvonne, were standing on the porch.

Josefina walked up to them and asked politely, "Miss Yvette and Miss Yvonne, would you know anyone who might have lost a baby burro? This burro here?"

Yvette and Yvonne smiled at Josefina and simply said, "No, dear."

Josefina hugged Cap and skipped on toward the marketplace. When she got there, she could hardly believe her eyes. The marketplace was empty! All the people had taken their goods and had gone home to supper.

Josefina didn't know what to do. She was happy and sad at the same time. Now Cap belonged to her, but she had not sold the fruit. So she had no real leather shoes to give to her grandfather for his birthday.

She turned away from the marketplace and started to walk slowly home. As she passed Mr. Hippolyte's sugarcane fields, she was surprised to hear her name called. It was Mr. Hippolyte himself, leaning on the fence with his straw hat resting on his nose. "Why so sad, little one?" he asked.

Josefina tried to smile, but instead she started to cry. She cried so hard she thought she would never be able to stop long enough to tell Mr. Hippolyte her terrible trouble. Mr. Hippolyte just waited. At last Josefina wiped away her tears and told her story.

Mr. Hippolyte looked at Josefina a long time. Then he said, "It just happens that I have a new pair of real leather shoes. Would you consider trading Cap for the shoes?"

It was Josefina's turn to look at Mr. Hippolyte a long time. Then she nodded her head, afraid to speak for fear she would cry again.

While she waited for Mr. Hippolyte to return with the shoes, she tied the ribbons from her hair in Cap's mane. "Be good, my little playmate," she whispered. "I will never forget you."

When Josefina got home, it was almost dark. She cooked meat and vegetables in a big pot and cut up all the ripe fruit from her basket. She had just put the shoes in the middle of the table when Mr. February returned from the sugarcane fields. He stood there and smiled at Josefina. And Josefina stood there and smiled back. Then Mr. February put on his real leather shoes and kissed Josefina on top of her head.

"Poor Mr. Hippolyte," he said while they were eating. "He has a responsibility, not a very big one, but he thinks he cannot handle it alone. He wondered if you would take care of it for him."

Josefina stared at her grandfather. Mr. Hippolyte had a responsibility! She started to speak, but before she could say a word, the door slowly opened.

And in came a little black burro with ribbons tied in his mane!

There Isn't Time

There isn't time, there isn't time
To do the things I want to do,
With all the mountain-tops to climb,
And all the woods to wander through,
And all the seas to sail upon,
And everywhere there is to go,
And all the people, every one
Who lives upon the earth, to know.
There's only time, there's only time
To know a few, and do a few,
And then sit down and make a rhyme
About the rest I want to do.

Eleanor Farjeon

Much More to Know

The Dolphin:
Creature of the Sea

Not long ago a boat was moving through the rolling, blue waters of the Indian Ocean when its engine suddenly stopped. For a while the boat, with its four passengers, rocked dangerously about in the high waves. Then came a wave, bigger than the others, which tossed the boat high into the air. When it dropped back into the water, the boat turned on its side and sank.

Three of the passengers were drowned. But the fourth passenger, a young woman, was not drowned. She was a strong swimmer and knew the direction of the land. But she also knew that the waters were filled with sharks, and that a cut on her leg was leaving a thin ribbon of blood behind her as she swam. Within minutes, the sharks, perhaps eleven or twelve of them, were following the path of blood straight toward her.

Then a strange and wonderful thing happened. She saw two other creatures of the sea, not sharks, but dolphins. The dolphins moved in close and began guarding her against the circling sharks. When she grew so weary that she thought she would surely drown, the dolphins swam beneath her and held her up in the water while she rested. Finally she came to a buoy, climbed onto it, and remained there until she was rescued.

This is not the only known case of a dolphin saving a person's life. Another swimmer reported being caught in an undertow and dragged beneath the surface of the water. Just as it seemed certain that she would drown, an animal rushed in and pushed her so hard that she landed up on the sandy beach. There, several feet from shore, as if waiting to see that all was well, swam a dolphin.

Dolphins have also been known to aid one another in time of trouble. When one is sick or weak, another may swim beneath it and lift it up to fresh air.

Because a dolphin will aid human beings as well as other dolphins, it is one of the most interesting creatures of the sea.

The Playful Dolphin

Dolphins have been described as the most unbelievable of all wild creatures. They are certainly among the world's smartest animals. Tame dolphins have been taught to dive through rings, to catch rubber balls, and to roll over and over in the water. One dolphin was even taught to tow a board on which a girl and a small dog rode.

Dolphins are easy to train because they enjoy working and playing with human beings. They learn quickly and remember well.

One diver told about entering a saltwater tank where tame dolphins were kept. He held out a brightly colored rubber ring to the bravest young dolphin. It nodded its head, and the diver pitched the ring.

The dolphin turned smoothly and shot off like an arrow. In a flash it was back with the rubber ring around its nose and a teasing look in its eye. Another young dolphin nodded, and the diver pitched the ring again. Then all joined in the game.

Soon the diver tired of throwing the ring. But while one dolphin held his attention, another shot up behind him and grabbed the ring, daring him to get it back. The dolphin would come almost near enough to be caught, then swiftly back away. When the diver held out his arms, the dolphin turned its head. When the diver swam toward it, the dolphin dashed away, then stopped dead. Finally it surfaced and made a loud, laughing sound before swimming away. By now the diver had received the message. He was no longer playing with the dolphins—the dolphins were toying with him.

A year and a half later, the diver returned to the saltwater tank. Leaning over the edge, he looked down at his tame friends. One familiar dolphin stared up at him for a long time, its head high above water and its mouth wide open. Then, seeming to remember, the dolphin went for the same rubber ring with which it had played. It hung the ring around its nose, swam toward the diver, and pitched the ring into his hands. Then it made that strange, laughing noise. The diver tossed the ring back, and they continued the game as though they had left it only yesterday!

Surprise in a Cornfield

Dionisio Pulido lived near the small village of Parícutin in Mexico. One February morning he went out to till his cornfield, carrying his tools with him. Dionisio could feel the ground shaking beneath him as he walked along. But the ground had been shaking for nearly two weeks, so he was used to it.

"And what if the ground does shake?" he thought. "The field must be tilled if the corn is to grow."

74

But Dionisio Pulido did not do much tilling that day, for a thin ribbon of steam began rising from the ground. The steam was coming from a hole that was a few inches wide. Frightened by what he saw, Dionisio swiftly dashed out of the cornfield, leaving his tools lying on the ground.

What Dionisio Pulido had discovered was the beginning of a volcano. Within a few hours the opening in the earth's crust had grown to be thirty feet wide. Ashes were pouring out, along with the steam. By night the hole had begun to spit out cinders. As they fell to the ground, the cinders formed a cone. The next day the cone was over a hundred feet high.

When the volcano was two days old, a glowing stream of lava began flowing over the edge of the cone. This lava, or melted rock, had been forced through the earth's crust from deep below the surface. As the months went by, other streams of lava burst out at the base of the cone, spreading over the countryside.

At the end of two years, the cone was over a thousand feet high and was known as Parícutin volcano. Its lava and ashes had covered more than four square miles, killing all the plant life and forcing the people to find new homes.

The
Buried City

The village near Dionisio Pulido's farm was not the first to be covered by lava from a volcano. Nearly two thousand years earlier, two cities in Italy had been buried in much the same way.

One of these cities, Pompeii, was built at the edge of the sea near the foot of a great mountain. This mountain, named Vesuvius, was an old volcano that had not erupted for hundreds of years. The farmers who lived near Vesuvius believed the volcano was dead and would never erupt again. So they planted their crops all the way up the sides of the mountain.

But one day Vesuvius did erupt, pouring ashes and melted rocks over the land for miles around. Steam and falling cinders trapped people in their homes, making escape nearly impossible. By the time Vesuvius stopped erupting, the city was buried under layers of lava, and hundreds of people had lost their lives.

Pompeii was almost forgotten for over a thousand years. Stories were told about buried cities, but no one knew where they were. No one was even sure that the stories were true.

Then one day a farmer was digging a well and discovered some of the remains of Pompeii. Since then the city has been uncovered and is open to the public, allowing them to see hidden treasures of the past.

Today people from all parts of the world go to Italy to visit the dead city. They find streets laid out with large blocks of stone. They find walls of buildings still standing. They find churches and houses, shops and public baths. They find beautiful paintings, pots and pans—even bread that was burned when the fire rained upon the city.

Since Pompeii was buried, Vesuvius has erupted again and again, each time pouring out lava—a sign that the volcano is still very much alive.

How to Make a Model Volcano

Here are the things you will need:

3 cups of flour
1 cup of salt
1 plastic straw
1 cardboard tube, 4½" long
1 cardboard base, 6" x 8"
Water
Tape

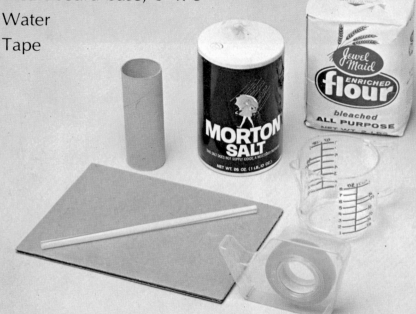

This is what you must do:

1. Mix the flour and salt together. Add water until the mixture feels like clay and is stiff enough to hold its shape.
   Note: Modeling clay may also be used.

2. Tape the plastic straw onto the cardboard base. Place the cardboard tube over one end of the straw and tape it to the base.

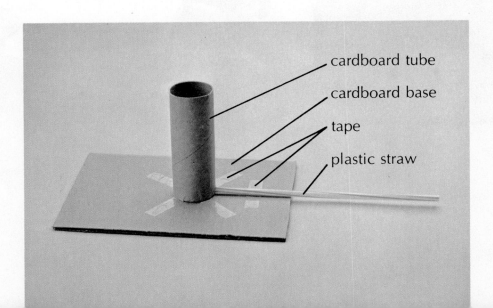

cardboard tube

cardboard base

tape

plastic straw

3. Form a cone-shaped mountain by spreading the claylike mixture over the sides of the tube and along the cardboard base. Be sure to leave the end of the plastic straw and the top of the tube open.

4. Now you have made a model volcano. Put it aside to dry.

5. You are now ready to make the lava mixture. You may mix some baking powder with a handful of sand. Or you could mix some flour with dirt.

6. Put the lava mixture in the top of the model volcano. Blow through the plastic straw. Now see what happens!

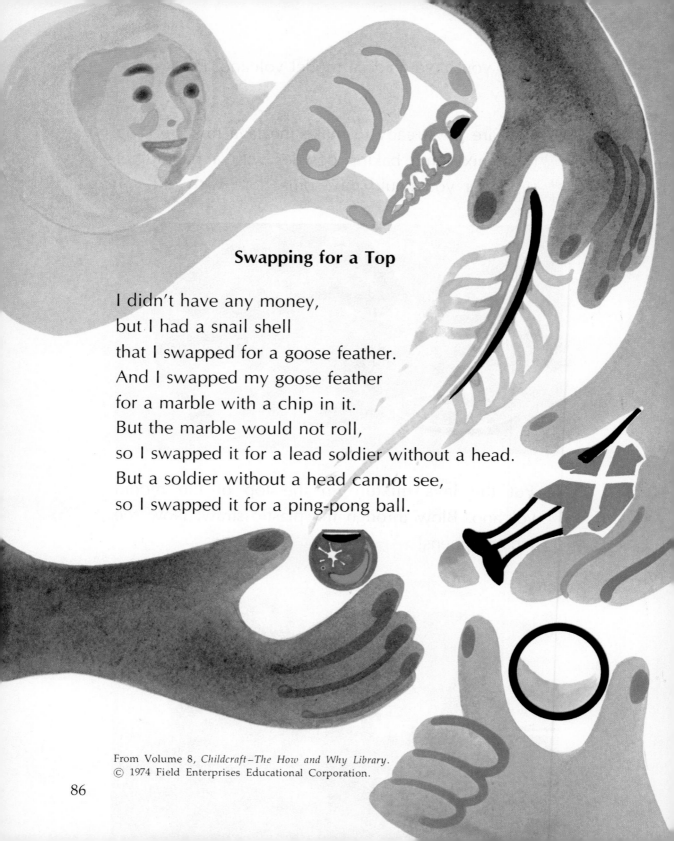

Swapping for a Top

I didn't have any money,
but I had a snail shell
that I swapped for a goose feather.
And I swapped my goose feather
for a marble with a chip in it.
But the marble would not roll,
so I swapped it for a lead soldier without a head.
But a soldier without a head cannot see,
so I swapped it for a ping-pong ball.

From Volume 8, *Childcraft—The How and Why Library*.
© 1974 Field Enterprises Educational Corporation.

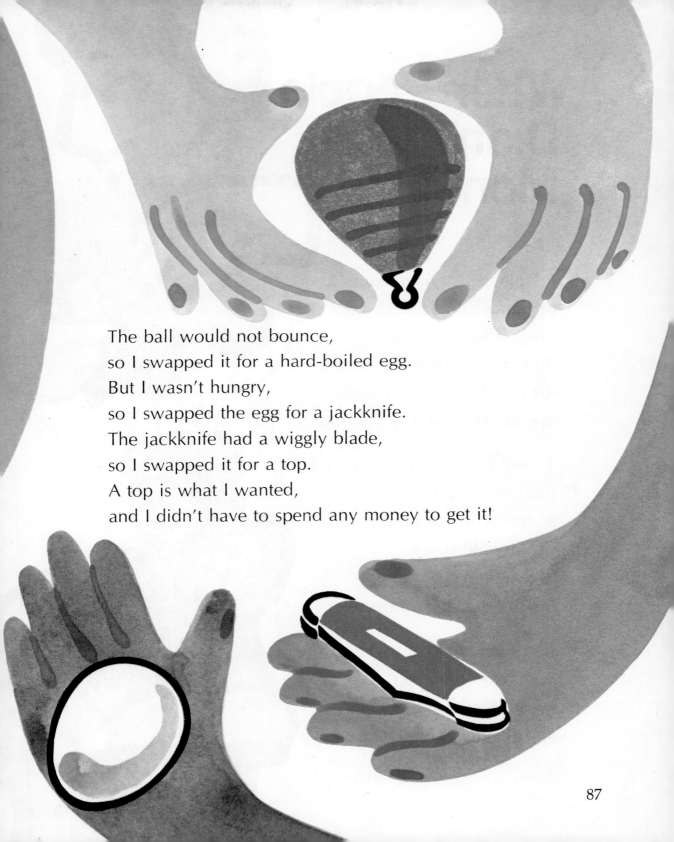

The ball would not bounce,
so I swapped it for a hard-boiled egg.
But I wasn't hungry,
so I swapped the egg for a jackknife.
The jackknife had a wiggly blade,
so I swapped it for a top.
A top is what I wanted,
and I didn't have to spend any money to get it!

When People Didn't Use Money

People didn't have coins
or paper money long ago.
They traded things
they owned or made
for the things they needed.
We call this kind of trading "barter."

To see how "barter" worked,
imagine you are
a shoemaker of long ago.
You would trade
the shoes you made
for the things you needed.

If you needed bread,
you gave the baker
a pair of working shoes
and he gave you some bread.

If you got hungry,
you gave the butcher
a pair of heavy boots
and he gave you some meat.

If you got chilly,
you gave the tailor
a pair of fancy shoes
and he gave you a coat.

Today, you still trade.
But instead of trading
the things you own or make,
you trade money
for the things you need.

IGLOOS ARE FOR TOURISTS

Bud Mayor stared out the window of the small airplane. Just imagine, a kid from Grove City on his way to a reindeer ranch in Alaska!

Bud's mother was a veterinarian and had been coming up here every year. That's how she met Meelak, an Eskimo who owned a reindeer herd. Several weeks ago a letter had arrived from Meelak, asking Doctor Mayor for her help. The Alaskan veterinarians thought there was something wrong with Meelak's reindeer, and he wanted Doctor Mayor to check the herd.

When Bud was invited to go along, he jumped at the chance. He'd never been to Alaska or met an Eskimo. And, like most tourists, he could hardly wait to see the igloos.

"We're almost there," said Doctor Mayor, breaking into Bud's happy thoughts.

The plane was circling. When it landed, dog teams and snowmobiles, towing long sleds, pulled up and started unloading the suitcases. Along with the other passengers, Bud and his mother gathered their belongings and left the plane.

"It's sure cold," said Bud as the wind swept across his face. When they neared the building, an Eskimo rushed out to meet them.

"Meelak!" cried Doctor Mayor, shaking hands with the Eskimo. "This is Bud."

"Young Bud Mayor," said the Eskimo, taking the boy's hand. "My son will be glad to see you."

The Mayors took their suitcases from a sled. Then they followed Meelak to a snowmobile, which took them to his reindeer ranch. Meelak's house was warm and cozy. His son, Meechek, welcomed them with a big smile. And Meelak's wife, Unalek, had a hot supper waiting for them.

The meat was delicious, and Bud willingly accepted a second helping.

"Like that meat, Son?" asked his mother, watching Bud heap the food onto his plate.

"You bet! Never tasted anything like this back in Grove City."

"Unalek is a good cook," said Meelak, smiling at his wife. "Walrus is a special treat of hers."

Bud started coughing, and the look in his mother's eye didn't help. "Well, it is good," he thought, "walrus or whatever." And he cleaned his whole plate.

After supper they sat by the fireplace and watched TV. "I expected to spend the night in an igloo!" Bud thought to himself. Then his interest switched to the subject his mother and Meelak were talking about.

"Reindeer supply many of the products we need," said Meelak. "We drink their milk, eat their meat, and use their hide to make leather. Reindeer are very valuable to the Eskimos."

"How do the herders get the reindeer to begin with?" asked Doctor Mayor.

"The government will lend reindeer to Eskimos who want to be herders," explained Meelak. "That's how I got my start. And we don't have to pay the government back until we have all the animals we need."

"I understand," said Doctor Mayor. "The government's lending program is a good idea. Then the supply of valuable products won't run low."

"We hope not," said Meelak.

"How many reindeer are in your herd?"

"We'll get an exact count tomorrow when you look at them. The wild animals have led some of my tame reindeer away, but I'd guess there are at least a hundred left."

"Sounds like a big day for us tomorrow. Better turn in, Bud."

So Meechek led Bud to his room. When Bud saw the twin beds piled high with blankets, he laughed out loud.

"What's the matter?" asked Meechek in alarm.

"I'm just laughing at myself," explained Bud as he sat on one of the beds. "I never thought I'd sleep in a house like this. I expected an igloo—with sleeping bags at best."

The boys laughed together. Finally Meechek said, "Most of the tourists think Eskimos live in igloos and ride in dogsleds. I can show you an igloo tomorrow if my father isn't using all the snowmobiles."

"All the snowmobiles!" exclaimed Bud. "How many do you have?"

"A number of them. We use them to drive the reindeer. Herders can use snowmobiles as neatly as your cowboys can use ponies."

"I'd sure like to watch them. And I'd like to see some igloos before I go home."

"You can do both," promised Meechek as the boys climbed into bed. Cozy and warm, they soon fell asleep.

The Rescue of Old Nellie

By the time the boys had finished breakfast the next morning, the men were rounding up the herd. The reindeer were moving at a fast pace. Whenever a few broke away from the herd, men on snowmobiles would race after them and bring them back. At times the noise sounded exactly like a sports-car speedway. The wind was cold, and a cloud of steam hung over the herd.

"We'll never get to use one of those snowmobiles," said Meechek. "I'll see if the men left any in the shed."

Bud was busy watching the herders when he heard his friend call, "They left Old Nellie."

"That's a funny name to hear in Alaska," laughed Bud. "Sounds more like a name somebody back home would call an old car."

"Well, there used to be a man who came up here to hunt. He always talked about his dog, Old Nellie, who was too old and too slow to hunt anymore. So Old Nellie seemed like a good name for this snowmobile. It's too slow for rounding up the reindeer. It'll keep running, though. Want to go see the igloos?"

"Sure."

The boys stopped by the house and told Unalek where they were going. "Meechek will lend you some warm clothes for the ride," she said to Bud. Soon they were on their way, dressed in bearskin pants, sealskin boots, and heavy jackets and wearing sunglasses.

Old Nellie slid over the crust of snow at a slow pace, but Bud enjoyed it. Snowmobiles were the big thing back home. There were all kinds of races for the older kids, and now there was even talk of having some night runs.

Bud was lost in thought when . . . thump! Old Nellie came to a dead stop.

"What's the matter?" asked Bud.

"Must have hit something," said Meechek. The boys got out and looked. The back end of the snowmobile was stuck in a hole.

"This is a river bed," explained Meechek. "Could be a hole where someone was fishing through the ice."

"What'll we do?"

"Try to push ourselves out."

"OK, I'll push, you drive."

Though the boys worked hard, they couldn't lift the snowmobile out of the hole. Finally they sat down to rest.

"Hungry?" asked Meechek.

"A little."

"I thought we'd be eating lunch in my friend's igloo by now."

"What's going to happen?" asked Bud.

"We'll be all right. Some hunter with a dog team will find us. Or my father will come looking for us when it gets dark. I'm glad I told my mother where we were going."

Bud nodded. "How cold is it?"

"Way below freezing," said Meechek. "Good thing my mother told me to lend you some of my clothes. Your own boots and jacket wouldn't have been warm enough. But we won't have long to wait. In the wintertime it gets dark about three o'clock."

Bud didn't feel as sure as Meechek, but he tried not to show it. Looking at his watch, he knew that there was more than an hour of daylight left.

The boys sat and talked. "Say, I think there's a rope here somewhere," said Meechek, poking about the floor and under the seat of the snowmobile. "Do you suppose we can do anything at all with it?"

"Let's tie it on the back. Maybe if we could pull Old Nellie a little to the side, you could drive her out."

Though they tugged and pushed, the snowmobile wouldn't move an inch.

When it began to get dark, Bud was uneasy. "They'll never find us," he thought. "No one has passed this way all day."

Meechek flashed the headlight on and off, hoping someone would spot it. Finally the boys saw another light coming up behind them. It grew brighter and bigger until it was almost upon them. It was Meelak with Doctor Mayor and another man. The boys were safe! The men would tow them out of the hole.

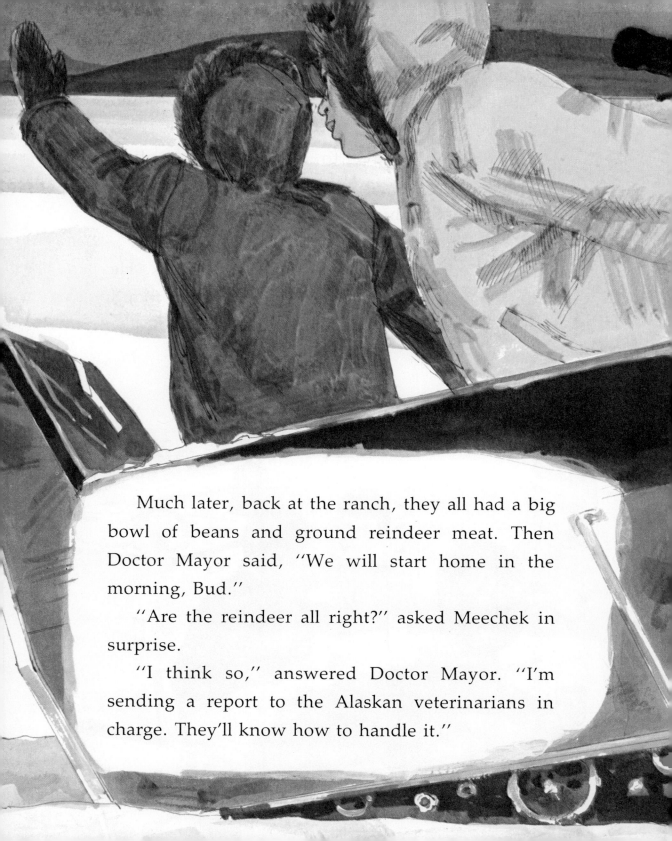

Much later, back at the ranch, they all had a big bowl of beans and ground reindeer meat. Then Doctor Mayor said, "We will start home in the morning, Bud."

"Are the reindeer all right?" asked Meechek in surprise.

"I think so," answered Doctor Mayor. "I'm sending a report to the Alaskan veterinarians in charge. They'll know how to handle it."

"I am grateful for your help," said Meelak.

"But if we go home in the morning, I won't get to see the igloos!" cried Bud.

"Then you'll have to come back," replied Meechek.

Bud looked at his mother, who nodded. "I'll be back," he said.

And Bud knew that he would come back. He hadn't seen the igloos this trip, but he'd found something much better—a new friend.

The Tsar's Riddles

Two brothers were making a trip on horseback. One brother was wealthy and lived by himself. The other brother was poor and lived with his eight-year-old daughter.

The wealthy brother's horse was hitched to a cart. The poor brother didn't even have a cart—only his horse, which was a mare.

They stopped for the night at a place along the way. After hitching the horses to a tree, both brothers fell asleep. Sometime during the night the mare had a colt. As soon as it could get up on its shaky legs, the little colt went over and stood under the cart.

In the morning the wealthy man woke his brother with a shout. "Get up quickly," he exclaimed, "and see what's happened. During the night my cart had a colt!"

His brother got up, saying, "Impossible! How could your cart have a colt? It was my mare that had the colt."

"You're wrong," the other replied. "If your mare had been the colt's mother, the colt would have stood under her instead of under the cart."

The brothers took their argument to court. The judge listened to the story each brother told, but he could not make up his mind. He soon grew tired of listening to their arguments and sent them away. So the case went from one court to another until it reached the Tsar's court.

Now the Tsar had his own way of doing things. When he called the two brothers before him, he said, "Here are four riddles you must solve. Of all things in the world, what is the strongest and fastest, what is the fattest, what is the softest, and what is the sweetest? Come back in three days and give me your answers."

The wealthy brother began to think very hard.
He didn't think of any answers, but he thought of
a woman who might help him, so he went to her
house.

"I am due back at the Tsar's court in three
days," he explained. "I must have the answers to
four riddles. Tell me, what is the strongest and
fastest thing in the world?"

"Why, that's easy!" said the woman. "There's
nothing in the world stronger or faster than my
husband's mare. She runs even faster than a
rabbit."

"What's the fattest thing in the world?" asked the wealthy brother.

"That black-and-white pig of mine!" exclaimed the woman. "It is so fat it can hardly stand."

"Of all things in the world, what is the softest?" questioned the man.

"Why, a featherbed, of course! Anybody knows that!"

"Now, this is the last question," said the brother. "What is the sweetest thing anywhere in the world?"

"The sweetest thing anywhere in the world is my little baby grandson."

"Thank you, my friend," said the wealthy brother. "I am grateful for your help."

The poor man returned home. His daughter, Natasha, saw him frowning hopelessly. "What's the matter, Papa?" she asked. "What makes you sigh and cry like that?"

"How can I help sighing and crying? In three days I am due back in the Tsar's court. He has ordered me to answer four riddles that I won't ever be able to figure out."

"What are the riddles?" asked Natasha.

When her father told her, the little girl said, "Papa, you must go back to the Tsar, and here is what you must tell him. The strongest and fastest thing in the world is the wind. The fattest thing is the land because it produces everything that grows, and it feeds everything that lives. The softest thing is a person's hand because it can be used for a pillow. And the sweetest thing in the whole world is sleep."

Natasha's Riddles

Both brothers went back to the Tsar and gave their answers. When they were through, the Tsar did not even look at the wealthy brother. Instead he asked the poor one, "Did you figure out those answers by yourself, or did somebody teach you?"

"Your Highness," said the poor brother, "I have a charming little daughter, who is only eight years old. She taught me."

"I see," said the Tsar. "Well, if your little girl is so clever, here's something for her to do. Give her this silk thread and tell her to produce a fine piece of cloth by morning."

The man took the silk thread and went home with it. As soon as his daughter saw him, she could see that he was sad. "All is lost," he told her, wringing his hands. "The Tsar has ordered you to make cloth from this silk thread."

"Don't be sad, Papa," said Natasha in her charming way. She broke off a twig from a branch and gave it to her father. "Take this to the Tsar and tell him to find a workman who can make a loom out of this twig. If the loom can be made, I'll have something on which to make the cloth."

Her father told the Tsar. The Tsar listened and gave him one hundred eggs. "Give these to your daughter," he said, "and tell her I demand that one hundred baby chicks hatch by tomorrow morning."

The poor man went home. "What a shame!" he cried when he got there. Then he told his daughter what the Tsar had demanded.

But Natasha just said, "You mustn't be so sad, Papa." She took the eggs and boiled all one hundred of them. Then she set them aside for their supper that evening.

"Now, Papa," she told her father, "go back to the Tsar and tell him the baby chicks will need a special kind of feed called one-day wheat. That means the wheat must be planted and full-grown, all in one day. Tell him that one-day wheat is the only kind baby chicks will eat."

So the poor man returned to the palace and told the Tsar about the one-day wheat.

When the Tsar heard this, he said, "If your daughter is so clever, let her appear before me tomorrow morning. Let her come not on foot and not on horseback, not with a gift and not empty-handed."

"Not even my daughter can manage to solve a riddle like that!" sighed the poor man, wringing his hands. "Now we are indeed lost."

But when he told her, Natasha said, "Don't be sad, Papa. Run along to the hunter's house and buy a live goat and a live pigeon."

The next morning she climbed upon the goat. Then she rode to the Tsar's palace, carrying the pigeon in her arms.

The Tsar met her at the palace gate. "Your Highness," she said in a charming voice as she got down from the goat, "here is a gift for you." The Tsar reached out his hands, but the pigeon flapped its wings and flew away.

"Very good," said the Tsar. "You have done everything I demanded. Now tell me one thing. If your father is such a poor man, how do you manage to eat?"

"My father catches fish on dry land, and I carry them home and make fish soup."

"You are not very smart!" shouted the Tsar. "When did a fish ever live on dry land?"

"You're not so smart, either!" exclaimed Natasha. "When did a cart ever have a colt? Colts come from mares, not carts!"

So the Tsar ordered his men to give the colt to the poor man. Then he brought Natasha and her father to the palace, where they lived a long and happy life.

THE STORM

Ko was always into some kind of mischief. Being a playful boy, he never really meant to do any harm. It was just that he always ran into trouble when he tried to help others or himself.

One day, after having worked many long weeks making his first canoe, Ko stood back and looked at it. "It's finished!" he thought. "I can hardly wait to put it into the water."

Just then Ko's father said, "Do not go out in your canoe today. There is a storm coming, and it will be too dangerous."

Ko was very disappointed to hear this. He had worked hard building the canoe, and now, when it was ready to sail, his father had said No.

"I am the best sailor of all," said Ko to himself. "I know it will not storm. The sun is so bright that the tops of the waves are shining from its light. My father always worries! But he didn't say I couldn't get the canoe wet."

And with that, Ko gave his canoe a small push . . . and then another . . . and then another . . . and then another. Finally it floated along near the water's edge.

Ko became so excited that he forgot what his father had just told him about the storm, and he climbed into the canoe.

"I will obey my father," he said. "I will just sit in the canoe to see if it leaks. That is what I need to know. After all, a good sailor would make sure a canoe does not leak before taking it out."

The paddle was in his way, and Ko could only think of one place to put it—in the water! He pushed the paddle into the water, and the canoe began to move. Again and again he pushed the paddle into the water. Any moment Ko expected to hear his father's angry voice calling him back. But he heard no voice, and so he became more and more daring.

The little canoe seemed to fairly fly. Before Ko knew it, he was far out in the ocean. When he looked back, the island had almost disappeared.

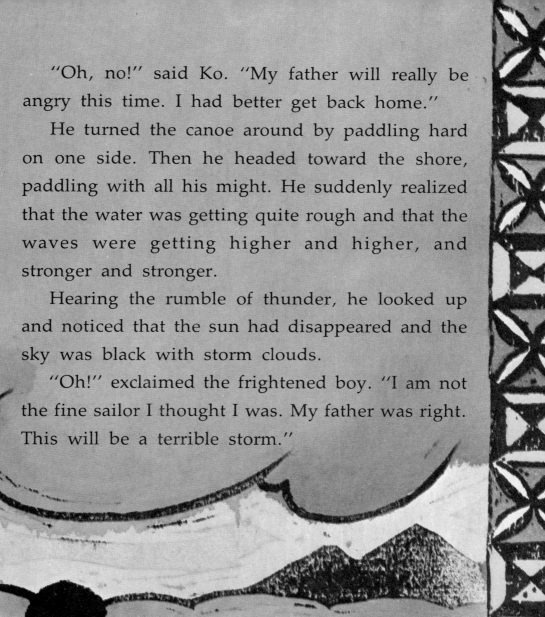

"Oh, no!" said Ko. "My father will really be angry this time. I had better get back home."

He turned the canoe around by paddling hard on one side. Then he headed toward the shore, paddling with all his might. He suddenly realized that the water was getting quite rough and that the waves were getting higher and higher, and stronger and stronger.

Hearing the rumble of thunder, he looked up and noticed that the sun had disappeared and the sky was black with storm clouds.

"Oh!" exclaimed the frightened boy. "I am not the fine sailor I thought I was. My father was right. This will be a terrible storm."

He tried to paddle the canoe in a straight line toward the beach, but the wind and the waves were too strong for his small arms. Wave after wave pitched him high in the air. The canoe went up one side of a wave and then down the other side, until suddenly a very large wave rose up in front of Ko! Higher . . . and higher . . . and higher . . . and higher it rose!

Finally the wave got so high that all Ko could see was a mountain of water. Then the rumble came again, this time louder than before. He closed his eyes and hid his head.

The wave broke and started to crash down on him. Then suddenly Ko felt himself going up, and up, and up.

"This is very odd," he cried in surprise, with his eyes still closed. "I should be going down, down, down—under the water, and yet I am high above the water!"

Ko decided to open his eyes very slowly to see where he was. First one eye, and then the other. "Why, I'm not even in the water!" he screamed. "Leaping Ula-Ula! I must be flying! My goodness, I had better flap my arms and kick my feet to keep going, or I'll surely fall into the ocean."

And with that, he began to wave his arms and kick his feet.

"Ko," said a strange voice, "be still and stop wiggling around, or you'll fall."

"Who said that?" cried Ko.

"I did," said the voice.

"My goodness," cried Ko, still waving his arms and kicking his feet. "I must be hearing things. Who could be talking to me way up here when I am flying? And how did I get up here in the sky when I should be down there in the water? I didn't know that I could fly. I didn't know just how wonderful I am! When I get home and fly right into the village, everyone will think I'm a hero."

He gave a very hard flap with his arms, turned his head to look up, and . . .

"Leaping Ula-Ula!" he cried. "Who are you? Whoever you are, please keep out of my way, or I'll bump into you. I've just learned to fly, you see, and I don't know how to steer too well."

"Don't you remember me?" asked the voice. "I'm Nui-Manu, the bird you saved from starving. I was lying on the beach with a broken wing. You fixed my wing and fed me until I could fly again."

Ko stopped wiggling and flapping and kicking. He looked up at the large bird that was holding him by the seat of his sarong.

"You mean that I'm not flying by myself?" he cried. "Now I won't be a hero when I get home. And my father will surely punish me. Oh, I'm so disappointed."

Then Ko quickly said, "I'm sorry. I didn't mean that I was disappointed in seeing you again. But I thought I was really flying by myself, and that would have made me a hero."

125

"Little Ko," said Nui-Manu, "you are as silly as ever. Now I must take you back to the island, or your parents will think you are lost."

"Oh, no!" cried Ko. "My father will really be angry this time. He told me not to go out in my canoe. But I thought I was such a good sailor that I went anyway. I can't go home! Please take me to where you live!"

"Little Ko," said Nui-Manu, "I agree that your father will surely punish you, but after all, you should be punished. However, if you wish to spend some time thinking, you may come to the Bird Rock that we birds use as our home. We will let your father know you are safe. The other birds will not bother you, and there are holes in the rock that will protect you from the weather."

"Then I will go with you," decided Ko with a shake of his head.

So Nui-Manu flew far out over the ocean, still carrying Ko by the seat of his sarong. She came to a large rock that rose straight up out of the water. There was no beach. Just straight sides that went up, and up, and up.

"This is my home, little Ko," said Nui-Manu as she set him down in front of a large opening in the rock. "This cave will keep you dry and protect you from the storms. And I will supply you with food so you do not starve."

For a few days Ko was very happy on the rock. The weather was fine, and the sun shone brightly. He swam in the water, and he played with the baby birds in their nests. He sat and talked to the older birds in the flock and listened while they told him of strange, far-off places where they had been.

Fooled by the Birds

Ko soon got tired of eating raw fish and not having his island playmates. He missed his mother and father very much.

Ko was homesick!

Finally the time came when he couldn't smile anymore and when he wouldn't eat any more. He wanted only to go home and see his father and mother. And, as the days slowly passed, he grew even thinner and sadder.

"How I pity little Ko!" Nui-Manu told the other birds sadly. "He is homesick and starving himself. He must return to his family."

"But we cannot make Ko go home," said one of the birds.

"No," replied Nui-Manu, "but if we try very hard, we will think of a way. Ko wants to go home, but he is afraid of being punished by his father."

Then the oldest bird in the flock said, "I believe I know how we can get Ko to go back to his family."

"How? How?" asked all the other birds. For they also pitied Ko and wanted to help him.

"You know how Ko has begged us to teach him to fly. Let us pretend to give him a lesson. Nui-Manu will take him high into the sky and tell him to flap his arms and kick his feet. While Ko is trying hard to stay up in the air, we will fly in circles around him. We must make him think that he is doing very well so he will not notice we are flying him toward the island."

"Wonderful! Wonderful!" cried all the birds. "Let's start right now."

So Nui-Manu flew to where Ko was living and said, "The birds tell me I have been unkind because I have not taught you to fly. You have asked many times, so today I will give you your first lesson."

"Leaping Ula-Ula!" cried Ko, smiling his first smile in many days.

He instantly jumped straight off the rock and began to wave his arms! Nui-Manu caught Ko by the seat of his red sarong before he fell into the water!

"Ko," she said, "you are going to have to be more careful. Now listen to me. When I say 'Now,' slowly flap your arms and kick your feet. The other birds in the flock will fly around you and make sure that you are doing everything just right."

So Ko got ready for his first flying lesson. When Nui-Manu said, "Now," he flapped and kicked, and kicked and flapped, and flapped and kicked some more.

"Everybody . . . hey, all you birds! Look at me! I'm flying! I'm flying! I'll be a hero after all," Ko yelled happily.

Suddenly Ko noticed that the flock had turned back. "Nui-Manu," he cried, "where are the birds? Where have they gone?"

"We have reached your home, Ko," the big bird said, "and it is time you were back with your family. The other birds have gone to the Bird Rock. Now I will let you down, and you can swim ashore. We will miss you, little Ko. Do not forget us, and maybe someday we will see each other again."

Then Nui-Manu flew close to the water and placed Ko in the waves. "Take care," she said, "and don't forget that it is much wiser to always obey your parents."

And with one great beat of her wings, she flew higher and higher until she was out of sight.

"Leaping Ula-Ula," said Ko to himself. "What a wonderful adventure! I know that none of my friends will ever believe that I once could fly."

He started swimming toward the beach, and when he could touch the bottom with his feet, he stood up and ran toward the sand.

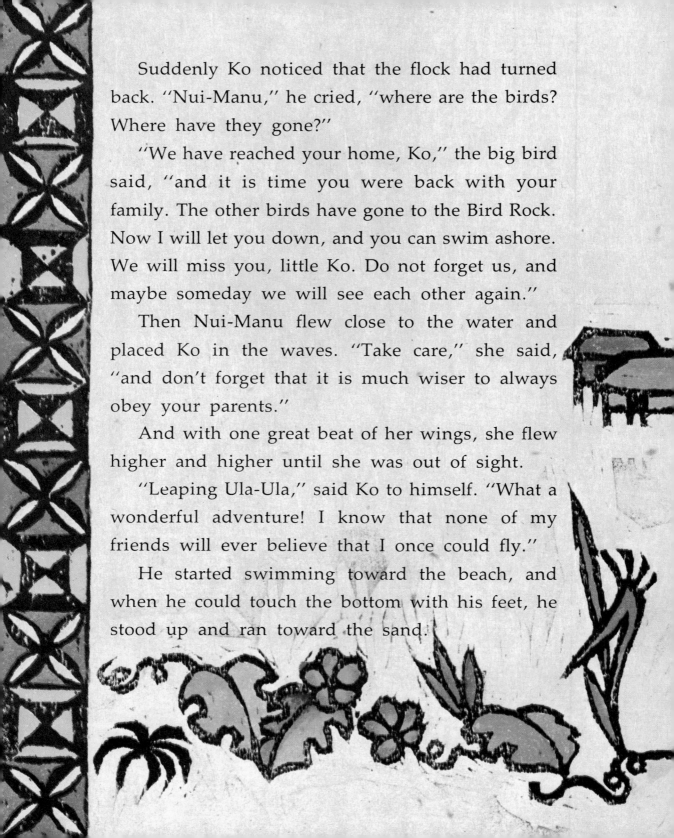

"I can't wait to see my mother and father," he cried, "even if I do get punished!"

And a wiser and much more grown-up boy ran to his house. He stood in the doorway with a smile on his face and with his chest stuck out—but with his hands covering the back of his red sarong.

Beware the Man
Without a Beard

Many years ago, on the island of Pontos, a boy
named Niko set out on his very first journey to
the marketplace. Along with him was his horse,
carrying huge baskets heaped high with grapes.

As Niko walked along he remembered his mother's parting words. "Beware the man without a beard," she had said. "If you meet such a man, return home at once, for your journey will not bring good fortune."

After he had passed the halfway mark on the road, he saw a beardless man coming toward him.

"Good day to you, my fine young lad," called the beardless man in a merry voice.

Niko remembered his mother's warning, so without a word he turned around and hurried home.

The next day Niko and his horse, loaded with baskets of grapes, again set out for the market. Once more he found himself facing the beardless man on the road.

"Good day to you, my fine young lad," sang out the beardless man.

"Good day," Niko replied faintly.

"These grapes, are they not for sale?" asked the beardless man.

"Yes, they are, but I won't trade with a beardless man. My mother has warned that such a trade will not bring good fortune."

"My fine lad," said the beardless man merrily, "don't you know you are in a place full of beardless men? From here to the marketplace, there are no bearded men to be found. Sell me the grapes, and I will give you a good price."

Niko considered for a moment. Since he had never been very far from home, he was not sure that the beardless man was telling the truth. But after some thought he agreed to the sale. The two made a deal, deciding that the grapes were worth eighty drachmas.

They then went to the barn of the beardless man, where Niko unloaded the grapes. As the boy started to lead his horse away, the man pushed him aside.

"Just a minute," he growled in a rough voice. "I bought the grapes and the horse as well for the eighty drachmas." With these words, the beardless man led the horse into the barn and locked the door.

Tears came to Niko's eyes. But the young boy realized he could not defend himself against a man who was much bigger and stronger than he. So he accepted the money and went back home with a heavy heart.

When he arrived home, the boy told his mother how he had been cheated and robbed of their only horse. She shed many a tear, then scolded him for not obeying her.

A few days later she called to him, "Niko, load our little donkey with these baskets of grapes and once again make the journey to the market. I will give you our last gold coins. With the coins and the money from the grapes, you must buy another horse."

Once again Niko set out for the marketplace, the donkey close at his heels. He had hardly passed the halfway mark when he saw the beardless man coming toward him.

"Well, my fine young lad, off to the market again?" hissed the man, grabbing Niko by the arm. "I see no need for you to go to the market when you can sell the grapes to me."

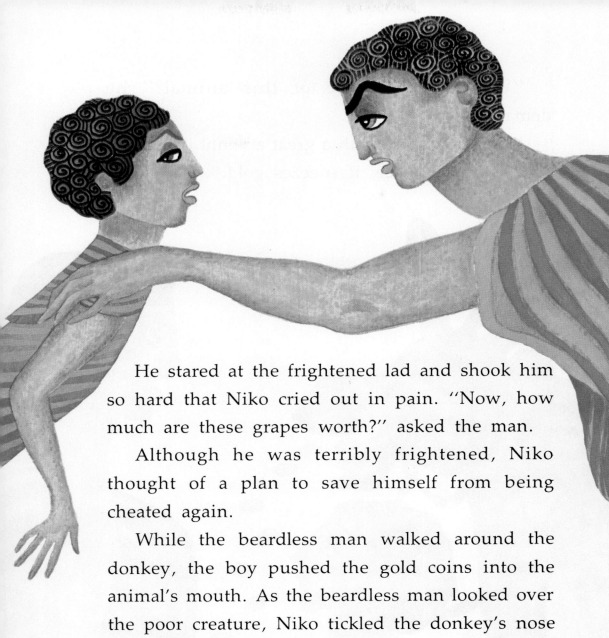

He stared at the frightened lad and shook him so hard that Niko cried out in pain. "Now, how much are these grapes worth?" asked the man.

Although he was terribly frightened, Niko thought of a plan to save himself from being cheated again.

While the beardless man walked around the donkey, the boy pushed the gold coins into the animal's mouth. As the beardless man looked over the poor creature, Niko tickled the donkey's nose with a straw. Suddenly the donkey sneezed, and out popped the gold coins. The beardless man could hardly believe his eyes.

"What is the price of this animal?" he
demanded.

"I'm afraid it's worth a great amount of money,
sir. As you can see, it sneezes gold."

"Never mind. Just tell me the price," ordered the man.

Niko thought carefully for several minutes. Finally he spoke. "I can let you have the donkey for six hundred drachmas."

Quickly the beardless man counted out the money and pushed it into Niko's hand. As the man led the donkey away, Niko called out, "If you want the donkey to sneeze coins all the time, you must put it in the cellar. Keep the door nailed closed for forty days and nights. Inside the house, dig a hole down to the cellar and pour water and throw grain down to the donkey. Afterward, open the cellar, and you will find it full of many gold coins."

Dancing with joy, Niko went home and told his family of his second meeting with the beardless man. Before his mother could scold him, the boy showed her the money he had received. Then he promised to go to the market the very next day to buy a fine horse. His mother was delighted because Niko's clever trading had brought them such good fortune.

The Best Trick of All

The next forty days seemed endless to the beardless man and his wife. On the evening of the last day, they excitedly opened the cellar door. Imagine how disappointed they felt when they found no gold coins on the cellar floor! Filled with anger, the beardless man ran down the road and across the field to Niko's house.

The boy was standing in the garden when he saw the man hurrying toward his home.

"Mother!" cried the lad, rushing into the kitchen. "When the beardless man asks for me, say that I am in the grove, but that you will send our dog to tell me to come home." With these words, the boy ran out and found a hiding place in the corner of the yard.

"Where is Niko?" roared the man as he pushed open the door.

"My dear man," answered the mother in a charming voice, "Niko is working in the grove. I will send the dog for him. The dog will tell him to come home so you may speak with him."

"What!" shouted the beardless man. "How can a dog tell Niko to return?"

"You will see," answered the mother. "Since we do not have a servant, we simply use our dog. We always send it to the fields with food or messages."

Niko's mother then opened the door and tapped the dog on its tail, saying, "Go tell Niko to come home. This man wants to speak to him."

When Niko saw his pet, he waved his hand so the dog would come to him. The boy and the dog hid in the yard for a few minutes. Then they went back into the house together.

When the beardless man saw Niko, he did not scold him. Instead he said, "I will forgive you, my lad, if you agree to sell me this dog."

"No, never!" cried Niko. "It is our servant."

But at last a deal was made, and the dog was sold for one thousand drachmas.

Singing and whistling a merry tune, the beardless man arrived home with the dog. Instead of smiles from his wife, he got a scolding for allowing himself to be cheated again.

The beardless man wanted to prove that this valuable dog would be their servant. The next morning he told his wife to put a lunch in a bag around the dog's neck. He told her to send the dog to the field where he would be working.

At the lunch hour, the man's wife opened the door, and giving the dog a pat on the tail, said, "Take this food to your master." But the dog ran into the yard and ate the food.

The next morning the angry man set out to see the young Niko and demand his money back. The lad was working in the fields when he saw the man and the dog coming toward him.

Throwing down his tools, he ran home and asked his mother and brother, Georgios, to help him again. "This time we must play the best trick of all," he said. While they listened, Niko described his plan.

When the beardless man would say that he had been cheated, Niko would blame his brother. He would pretend to argue with Georgios, and in a fit of anger, would slap him. Georgios would sink to the ground and pretend to be dead.

"When you hear me play my flute," continued Niko, "you must rise up and make believe you have come back to life."

No sooner had he finished explaining the plan than the door flew open, and the beardless man rushed in. "You've cheated me for the last time. This dog can do nothing! Give me back my thousand drachmas."

At that point the boys began to argue, blaming one another for planning the trick. Niko gave Georgios a heavy slap, sending him to the floor. The beardless man shouted, "Now see what you have done. You have killed your brother!"

"Fear not, sir," replied Niko. "What I have done in anger can be made right." Then he began playing a gay tune on his flute. Georgios stirred, opened his eyes slowly, and got to his feet.

The man was speechless! Then he cried, "Niko, you have cheated me many times. But I will forget all that if you will sell me your flute."

At first Niko would not sell, but after a great deal of arguing, he agreed to part with the flute for two thousand drachmas.

Once again the man went home, feeling quite merry. He burst into the house, where he found his wife and her relatives drinking coffee. He proudly showed them the flute.

Much to his surprise, his wife began wringing her hands hopelessly. "Alas!" she exclaimed. "We shall die of hunger! You have been cheated of all the money we had left."

The beardless man, sure that the flute was magic, decided to teach his wife and her relatives a lesson. "Stop arguing with me!" he yelled. "We will not die of hunger." He ran to the kitchen and picked up a dead chicken which his wife had planned to cook for their dinner.

"Dear wife and relatives," he said, "just see how valuable this instrument is." And he began playing a gay tune on the flute. But nothing happened to the chicken. Again he played the tune. Still nothing happened. The creature did not stir. For a moment the beardless man was speechless. He could hardly believe his eyes.

"But . . . but the flute is magic!" he cried. "The chicken is supposed to come to life."

His wife and her relatives began slapping him for being so foolish. He tried to protect himself and finally ran to the barn. "Alas!" he thought sadly to himself. "I paid too high a price for the horse I took from Niko."

What did the beardless man mean when he said, "I paid too high a price for the horse I took from Niko"?

Sky Country

In a faraway village there once lived two boys who were great friends. Although their homes were in different parts of the village, Lunaxa and Galwet would go back and forth to each other's house so they could be together. The boys spent most of their time making arrows which they would shoot into the air.

Just in back of the village was a grassy hill where the boys often played. They liked to shoot arrows from the hillside into a field nearby.

One fine night when the moon was shining, they decided to climb to the top of the hill. As they were going along, Lunaxa said, "Look at the moon, Galwet. See how ugly it looks. It's not nearly as beautiful as the sun."

"Hush!" whispered Galwet. "You must not talk that way. The moon will be angry."

No sooner had Galwet spoken than darkness swept across the hillside. Out of the darkness appeared a rainbow, which formed a ring about the boys. Then, as quickly as it had come, the rainbow disappeared, and Galwet was left standing alone. Lunaxa was nowhere to be seen.

Galwet called and called, but he got no answer. "Lunaxa has run up the hill to get away from the rainbow," he decided. So Galwet climbed to the top, but his friend was not there.

High above, in the night sky, Galwet could see the moon. "The rainbow must have come from the moon," he thought. "The rainbow has taken Lunaxa up to the moon!" And Galwet sat down and cried.

Finally he wiped away his tears and looked toward the heavens. "I will shoot the star closest to the moon," he decided. So Galwet took careful aim and shot into the sky. In a moment the star darkened, but the arrow did not return. Galwet began shooting more arrows, each time aiming in the same direction. Again and again he aimed at the spot where the star had been.

When most of the arrows were gone, Galwet saw something hanging down from the sky. It was a chain of arrows—the very ones he had shot, each arrow joined to another. Now Galwet aimed at the chain. By the time the last arrow was shot, the chain reached the ground.

It had taken most of the night to shoot the arrows, so Galwet was tired. He lay down under the chain and fell asleep, dreaming about his lost friend. When he awoke, he remembered the chain of arrows. Looking up, he discovered that the chain was now a ladder reaching into the sky.

Although his fear was great, Galwet knew he must climb the ladder. First, however, he broke several branches from a nearby bush and stuck them into the knot of his hair. Then he began the long journey upward.

All day long he climbed. Night came, and the weary boy fell asleep. When he awoke, his head felt heavy, and he was hungry. Remembering the branches in his hair, he pulled one out and found it was loaded with ripe, red berries. After he had eaten his fill, Galwet felt strong enough to continue the upward journey.

Higher and higher he climbed, through layers of clouds, heavy with fog. By noon he was again hungry, so he pulled out another branch and ate the ripe fruit. Then on he went, not stopping until he reached the sky country.

It was midnight when Galwet discovered a lake.
He gathered some leaves and soft brush and lay
down to sleep.

Not long after midnight Galwet heard a soft
voice saying, "Wake up. I am coming for you."
The frightened boy sat up and looked but saw no
one. He tried to sleep again but failed. By and by
he saw a small, beautiful girl walking toward him.

"I have come after you," said the girl. "My
grandmother has sent me. I will take you to her
house."

The Chase

Galwet followed the girl until they came to a very small house. The grandmother invited them to enter and sit by the fire. As they watched the flames leaping upward, the woman turned to Galwet and asked, "Why have you come here?"

"To get Lunaxa, who was taken away," Galwet answered. "I climbed up the ladder to find him."

"I have pity for your friend," said the woman. "So I will help you. If you listen, you can hear him wailing. He is being punished in the moon's house."

"I will rescue him!" cried the boy, leaping to his feet.

The grandmother stretched out her arm. "You must eat first," she said, knowing that he was weak from hunger. Then, placing a hand over her mouth, she brought forth a salmon. "Eat this, my son."

After Galwet had eaten, she gave him a spruce cone, a tree branch, a rosebush, and a small stone. "These will protect you," she explained. Galwet thanked her and started on his way.

As Galwet drew near the moon's house, the crying and wailing became louder. Looking upward, Galwet discovered that Lunaxa had been put in the smoke hole. At any moment the flames would reach him.

Realizing the danger, Galwet climbed onto the roof as fast as he could. Then, stretching out his arm, he pulled his friend to safety.

He placed the spruce cone over the hole and told it to begin wailing, hoping to fool the moon. Within seconds, the boys had grabbed each other by the hand and were leaping from the roof.

But the wailing soon ended because the spruce cone was small and dropped into the flames below. The moon, realizing what had happened, started rolling after the boys.

Looking back, Galwet saw that the moon was gaining speed, so he threw the tree branch into the path. A great hole opened up right where the tree branch had landed. The moon could not stop rolling in time to keep from sliding into the hole.

Now the moon was angrier than ever, causing the earth to rumble and shake. Pulling itself out of the hole, the moon again started after the boys.

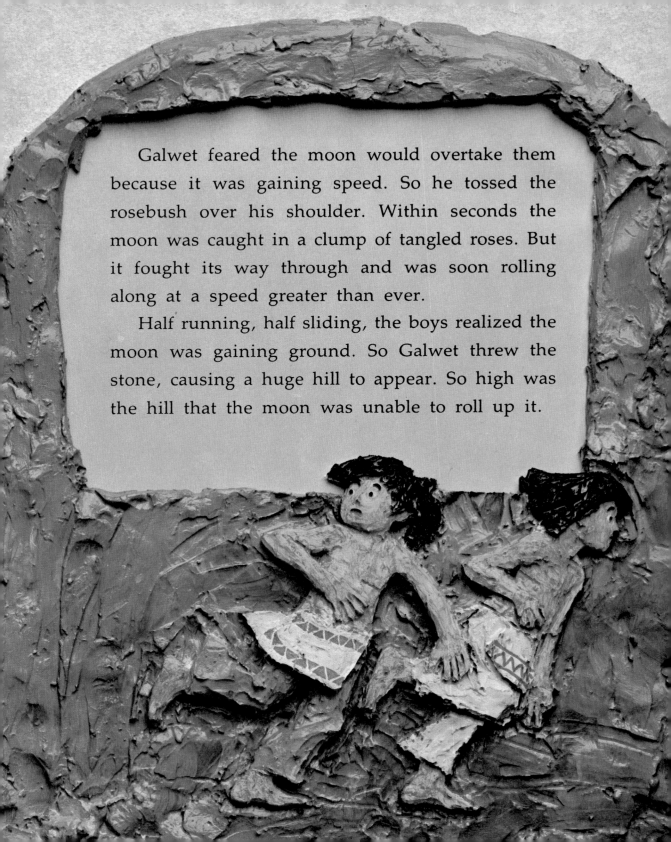

Galwet feared the moon would overtake them because it was gaining speed. So he tossed the rosebush over his shoulder. Within seconds the moon was caught in a clump of tangled roses. But it fought its way through and was soon rolling along at a speed greater than ever.

Half running, half sliding, the boys realized the moon was gaining ground. So Galwet threw the stone, causing a huge hill to appear. So high was the hill that the moon was unable to roll up it.

Galwet and Lunaxa reached the grandmother's house, tired but happy over their escape. After they had caught their breath, Galwet said, "We wish to return home. Will you help us?"

"Go and lie down where you have left the ladder," replied the woman. "Rest quietly and think about the place where you like to play."

Galwet and Lunaxa did as they were told. And when they awoke, they discovered they were lying on the grassy hillside where the ladder had been. Their arrows were heaped in a pile beside them. So happy were the boys to be back on earth that they did not stop to gather the arrows. Instead they ran into the village, where they were welcomed by their families and friends.

Everyone listened as they told their story. And from that day to this, no one in the village has spoken an unkind word about the moon.

Dream Song

as my eyes
search
the prairie
I feel the summer
in the spring

Chippewa

Art Is Where You Find It

Penny's Good Fortune

Penny's good fortune started one October day when she went into Mrs. Hobbs' secondhand store to buy a birthday present for her mother.

Mrs. Hobbs' store had everything from old chairs and dishes to used clothes and jewelry. Things were tossed about in baskets and boxes. Some were even piled up in the window. That was where Penny had first seen the brooch. It was there in the window, in a dusty, blue case. She had passed it every morning on her way to school.

The first day she saw the brooch, she started saving her money. And now, after three weeks, she had managed to save one dollar and sixty-five cents. "I hope it won't cost more than that," she sighed as she entered the store.

When the door opened, a bell rang to let Mrs. Hobbs know that a customer had arrived. Hearing the bell, she limped in from the back room where she lived. She was leaning on her cane.

She smiled at Penny and asked, "What can I do for you?"

"I'd like to buy the brooch in the window for my mother. How much is it?"

Mrs. Hobbs limped over to the window and brought the brooch back to the counter.

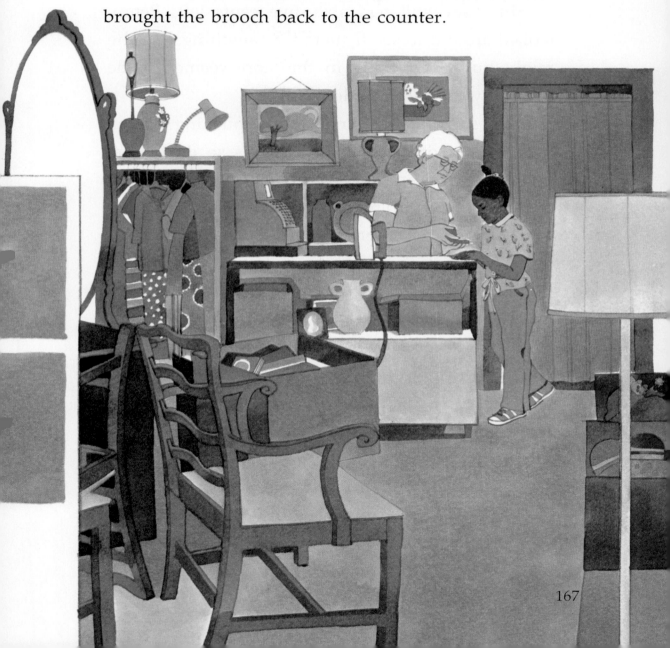

"Just a dollar," said Mrs. Hobbs, holding the case out for Penny to see.

"It's beautiful!" said Penny. "I'll polish it before I give it to my mother."

Since she still had sixty-five cents left, Penny looked around to see if there was anything else she might buy. Everything in the store seemed to be covered with fine, powdery dust.

"I'm sorry," said Mrs. Hobbs, pushing back a loose strand of hair. "Everything is so dusty that my customers can't see what I have. I expected to clean the place from top to bottom this summer, but here it is October, and I still haven't done it. This limp of mine has really slowed me down. And I don't have the money to pay someone to clean for me. I wish I did."

Penny stared at Mrs. Hobbs in surprise. "Why, you don't need to pay anyone!" she exclaimed. "I'll be glad to help you. All I need is some soap and water, and I'll have everything shining bright in no time."

"Oh, would you?" asked Mrs. Hobbs, her eyes glowing. "How old are you, dear?"

"I'm eleven," replied Penny. "I've been helping my mother with the work at home since I was eight. I'll come every afternoon right after school. Every afternoon except Thursday. That's when I go to art class at the museum. I'm going to be an artist some day."

Smiling gaily at Mrs. Hobbs, Penny opened the door to leave. The bell rang again. "It says hello and good-bye," thought Penny to herself.

Half running, half skipping, she headed down the alley toward home. She spent most of the evening polishing the brooch until it shone.

"Oh, honey," exclaimed Penny's mother when she saw the gift. "It's the loveliest thing I've ever had. But you should have spent the money on yourself."

Penny just smiled, pleased that her mother liked the present she had selected.

The next day Penny stopped at the store. She filled a bucket with soapy water and washed nearly everything in sight. She worked for over a week before the store started to take on a new look.

Then more customers began coming in, and the little bell rang merrily.

"Good heavens!" exclaimed Mrs. Hobbs. "You have done wonders with this place. And I'm selling more things than I ever dreamed was possible. I feel much better, too. So many customers stopping in have made me almost forget my limp. You've done me a big favor, and I would like to give you something, Penny. Look around the store and select anything you want."

Penny's choice was an easy one, for she knew exactly what she wanted. It was a small statue of a clown wearing a red mask, red and yellow tights, and a green jacket with purple patches.

Penny handled the statue carefully, looking longingly at the shiny, bright colors. She had loved it from the moment she saw it.

"You like the little clown statue, don't you?" Mrs. Hobbs said, watching her. "Then take it for your own. I want to return the favor you did for me. I'm glad you found something you like."

Joyfully Penny carried the little clown home. She showed it to her mother and then placed it on the dresser in her bedroom. There she could see the clown the last thing at night and the first thing in the morning.

Penny had wanted to be an artist ever since her first visit to the museum. She had stood speechless before the paintings of the great masters. She had walked on tiptoe around the glass cases filled with beautiful statues. "And now I have a statue as beautiful as any of them," she thought happily to herself.

Penny Makes a Choice

The following Thursday, when Penny went to art class, she took the statue along to show her teacher. He handled it almost lovingly. "It's beautiful," he said. "Where did you get it?" Penny explained about Mrs. Hobbs' store.

"May I show it to Mrs. Smith, the museum curator?" he asked. Penny agreed, so he took the statue to Mrs. Smith's office while the class continued painting.

In a few minutes the curator came in to talk with Penny. Mrs. Smith asked if she might take the statue to New York the next day.

"I'm going to a museum in New York," she explained. "I would like to show your clown to the curator there. He knows more about statues than I do. I believe this one may be quite valuable. Come upstairs with me, and I'll show you what I mean."

Penny followed the curator into a large room where priceless statues were kept. "See here," said Mrs. Smith, pointing out a statue. "That looks very much like your clown. It was made by a great artist many years ago. He made over a thousand different statues during his lifetime. Your statue has the same artist's touch, both in form and in color."

So Penny agreed to let Mrs. Smith take the little clown. She could hardly wait to tell her mother and Mrs. Hobbs what had happened. Mrs. Smith was due back from New York in several days, and they all looked forward to her return. Penny was sure Mrs. Smith would have good news.

She came back all smiles. Penny's clown was a valuable piece of art made by the same artist Mrs. Smith had told her about. It was worth thousands of dollars. The curator went on to explain how great art treasures were often sold to museums so they could be enjoyed by the public. She said that if Penny and her mother wanted to sell the little clown, she would arrange everything for them.

"I'll let you know tomorrow," said Penny.

Penny was not sure what she wanted to do. She hated to part with her treasure, but she knew her mother could use the money. It was a hard choice to make.

She thought about Mrs. Hobbs, too. "She should have some of the money. The clown was hers in the first place. She didn't realize that she was giving away something so valuable." Finally Penny decided to sell the statue.

So she and her mother went to see Mrs. Hobbs. They wanted to talk over the matter with her.

"I don't want any of the money!" exclaimed Mrs. Hobbs. "Penny did me a favor when I needed help. She's given me more happiness than I've known for a long time. Why, I even feel better. It's no wonder she's had this good fortune. She brings so much joy to others."

But Penny and her mother did not agree with Mrs. Hobbs. They finally decided that the money for the sale of the statue should be shared three ways. One third was to go to Mrs. Hobbs, one third to Penny's mother, and one third was to be saved for Penny's schooling.

Penny looked longingly at her dresser the night after Mrs. Smith took the little clown back to New York.

Then she smiled. "Mrs. Hobbs and Mother and I will all be much better off because of the statue. Mrs. Hobbs will have money to buy something special. Mother won't have to work so hard. Then someday when I'm an artist, I'll make something beautiful that will delight everyone who sees it, just as the statue does."

Then, closing her eyes, she drifted off to sleep. A colorful little clown danced through her dreams.

María Martínez, a Pueblo Potter

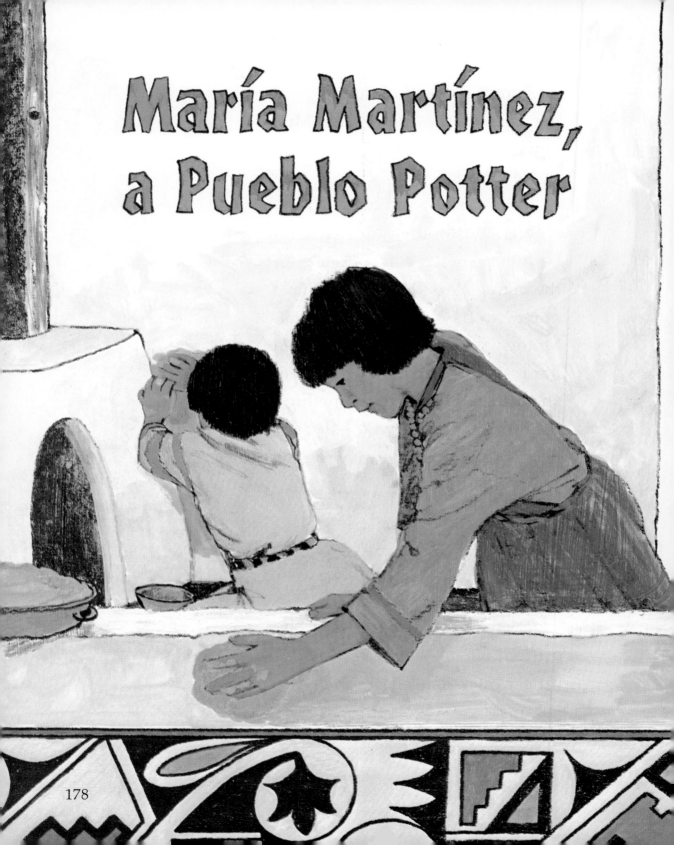

María Martínez, a gifted Indian potter, was born in New Mexico many years ago. She and her sisters lived with their parents in a pueblo, along with many other Indian families.

Nearly every day María helped her mother around the house. When her work was finished and the weather was warm, María was free to play in the playhouse with her younger sister. The girls had built the playhouse from mud and straw. Inside were two rooms—a room for María and a room for her sister. There was even a fireplace in each room.

The girls played in the playhouse, doing many of the things the pueblo women did as they worked in their homes. María and her sister swept the floor with brooms made by their father. They pretended their dolls were babies and practiced taking care of them, just as an Indian mother would do. And every year they made the playhouse bigger and better.

María and her sister enjoyed eating lunch in the playhouse and often shared the food with their friends. At first they used their mother's dishes, but María decided they should make dishes of their own. She thought it would be easy to dig the clay and shape it into bowls. She knew how to mix clay to make a fireplace or to build a wall, but she did not know how to keep the clay bowls from cracking. The girls tried again and again, but the bowls always cracked while drying in the hot sun. María finally decided they should ask Tía Nicolasa for help.

Tía Nicolasa, one of the best pottery makers in the pueblo, was willing to help the girls make their bowls. She had them sit with her on the shady side of the house, explaining that potters must work in the shade to help keep the clay damp.

Tía Nicolasa showed the girls how to mix sand with the clay to make it hold together. They watched with great interest as she started each bowl with a flat piece of clay shaped like a pancake.

They saw her roll some damp clay into sausages and wrap the sausages around the edge of the pancake. They saw how the bowl was smoothed inside and out so that none of the clay sausages would show.

María and her sister made some bowls of their own. They kept their bowls in the shade for two days and then placed them in the sun to harden. But the girls knew that real potters do not let their pottery harden in the sun. Instead the potters place their bowls over a fire prepared for that purpose.

Later that summer María learned how to build a pottery fire. She had made a jar with a tall neck. She had worked well, and Tía Nicolasa decided that the jar was worth firing. And so María learned to fire her own pottery. Her jar came out just right!

María never forgot the lessons she had learned from Tía Nicolasa. Many years later, when María was married, she found herself in the pottery-making business. With her husband, Julián, María turned pottery making into a fine art that brought honor and fortune to their pueblo.

María made many trips across the country, showing the pottery and receiving honors for her work. But she never forgot the pueblo way of life. She became a leader of her people and is thought of today as a "Mother of the Pueblo." And for María Martínez, this is perhaps the greatest honor of all.

María Martínez demonstrates the fine art of pottery making.

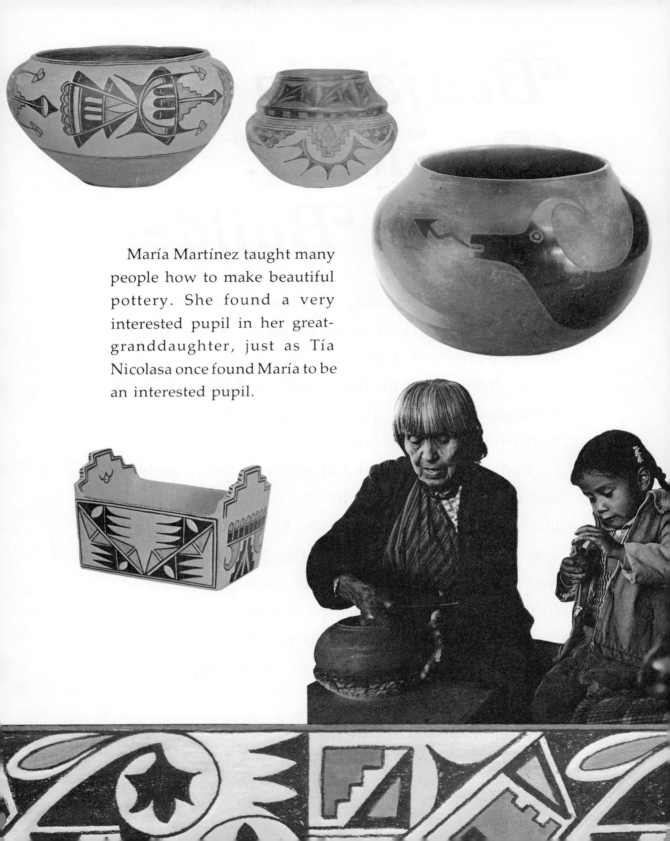

María Martínez taught many people how to make beautiful pottery. She found a very interested pupil in her great-granddaughter, just as Tía Nicolasa once found María to be an interested pupil.

Benjamin Banneker, the Builder

One winter evening Benjamin Banneker sat down at the kitchen table as soon as the supper dishes were cleared away.

In front of him he placed a large piece of hardwood and a pocket watch that he had borrowed from a friend.

Ben's mother pulled a chair close to the table so she could mend a coat by the light of the candle. His sister Minta leaned over his shoulder. Minta was a young woman, and she had never before had a chance to look closely at a watch. Few people in those days had a watch or a clock.

"How wonderful it would be to own that!" she said, touching the watch with her finger. "I could always know what time it is."

Holding the watch carefully in his left hand, Benjamin opened the case so he could see the busy wheels inside.

"Should you do that?" asked Minta in surprise. "It isn't your watch."

Ben smiled at her. "Wait till you see what I'm going to do next. I'm going to take it apart, but don't worry. The gentleman I borrowed it from said I could do whatever I wish, as long as I put it together again."

Ben's father and his sister Molly soon joined the other members of the family around the wooden table. Outside a cold wind whistled around the small log cabin, but flames from the fireplace kept the room cozy and warm. Now and then the howl of a wolf or the cry of a wildcat could be heard. Inside the only sound was the cracking of the logs in the fireplace.

One by one Ben removed the tiny wheels and gears, carefully remembering the way they were arranged in the watch. He knew it would be his responsibility to return the watch exactly as it had been given to him.

"Why are you taking all the pieces out of the watch?" asked Molly.

Ben wearily rubbed the back of his neck where it ached from bending over his work. "I'm going to make a clock," he explained. "I saw a picture of one that I'd like to copy. I'm sure I can make one after I study this watch."

"A clock!" Ben's mother let her mending drop into her lap. "How will you manage to do that? You don't have any metal or the right tools."

Ben put one hand onto the piece of hardwood that lay on the table. "I have some wood and a knife. I'll carve all the parts out of wood."

Several nights passed before he began to carve. First he had to measure the wheels and the gears and figure out the size that each one in his clock should be. As he worked, he was thankful that he had a good head for solving problems.

Every evening that winter he worked on his clock, often staying up till long past midnight. When summer came, he had less free time. But whenever he could take a moment from work on the farm, he continued to figure and to carve.

Carefully he made the gears. Every piece had to be exact. Often he would have a gear or a wheel almost finished, and a small slip of his knife would damage it. He would then have to throw out the part that was damaged and start all over.

The neighbors for miles around learned of Benjamin's undertaking and came to watch him. They knew that he was clever with his hands as well as with his mind. He was always making some kind of tool or something for the home. But this time, surely, he was trying to do something that no one could do. To make a clock of wood, with only a watch to copy, seemed impossible.

Even Benjamin sometimes felt defeated. After months of work he had all the carefully carved parts in place. His wooden clock had begun to look like a clock, but one problem still remained. He could not get the hour and the minute hands to move together at the proper speed.

Again and again he studied the workings of the borrowed watch. Again and again he took his clock apart and put it together. A year had passed since he first started to make it.

"Why don't you give up?" asked Molly. "It's a fine clock. What if one hand does run a little too fast?"

Ben set his lips tightly together, refusing to accept defeat. "It must keep perfect time."

Several days later Ben discovered the mistake in his work and set it right. When at last he saw the hands of the clock working together as they should, he felt at peace.

He placed his clock in a neat case and hung it on the wall.

Day after day and year after year, people came to see Benjamin Banneker's wooden clock that kept perfect time.

The borrowed watch, unharmed, was again in the pocket of its owner.

A City Is Born

A raw wind blew at Benjamin's coattail as he rode down the hill to the post office. He was cold, but he wanted to pick up his mail. There might be a letter with a problem for him to solve or a book he had ordered from overseas.

As Benjamin tied his horse to the rail in front of the general store, he saw Andrew Ellicott coming down the steps of the building.

Mr. Ellicott walked right up to Benjamin and shook hands with him, saying, "Come inside where it's warm. I have a favor to ask of you." He led the way into a tiny office behind the counter.

"Ben, President Washington plans to build a new city for our country's capital."

Benjamin nodded. "Yes, I know. And I know that he made a wise choice when he asked you to survey the land where it's going to be built."

Ben also knew that President Washington had asked several men to help with the survey and to lay out the streets for the new city.

Now Andrew Ellicott leaned forward excitedly. "Would you consider working with me?"

"You're joking!" replied Ben in a surprised voice.

"Not for a minute. What do you say, Ben?"

Benjamin smiled and said, "I feel safe in saying yes." He was sure he would not get the job. Still, he could not help dreaming. If he should be accepted, he might meet some important men who worked for the government. He might even see the President himself!

Benjamin put the matter out of his mind. It was no use thinking of something so wonderful—and so unlikely.

But several days later Andrew Ellicott came to him with the good news. "It's all settled," he said. "You're to help me survey the land."

For a moment Benjamin was speechless. Then he said, "I never expected to get the job, and I've agreed to write a book. It's due at the printer's by the end of the year."

"The survey for our country's capital must come first," replied Andrew. "Whatever service you give to your country is more important than any book. I'm sure you'll still have time to finish the book when you return home."

Benjamin took a deep breath. "I'll try."

In February, 1791, Ben set out on horseback for the forty-mile trip. As he rode along, he wondered how he would be accepted by the other men who were helping with the survey. They might be different from Mr. Ellicott, who never seemed to care that Benjamin's skin was black.

However, Ben need not have worried. His quick mind and good manners quickly won the friendship of the men. Besides, as Andrew had said, it was good to be of real service to his country.

The rough, woodsy land where the work began did not look as if it would ever become a city. Hundreds of trees had to be cut down before the men could even start the survey. They had to fight insects, snakes, mudholes, and thick tangles of trees and bushes.

But to Ben, the survey was exciting. Using Ellicott's instruments, Benjamin made sure the lines of the survey were straight and true.

Major L'Enfant had been placed in charge of all the planning for the capital city. L'Enfant was a clever man and had been carefully chosen. But he was quick to anger when his ideas were not accepted. Because of L'Enfant's many outbursts, the work was going very slowly.

Ben wished he could stay until the survey and the planning were finished. But he knew that he must go home before summer if he were to have his book ready in time for the printer.

Back home, Benjamin's sisters and their children wanted to hear all about the new city. They watched him draw a map in the dust.

"The most important building is going to be right here, in the center of the city," he told them. "It will be the building where the laws of our country will be made. The streets will go out from the center, just like the spokes of a wheel."

The children leaned over the map. They tried to imagine how the city would look.

"The streets will be wider than any you have ever seen," Benjamin explained. "Some streets will be as much as one hundred sixty feet wide."

It will be a beautiful city, thought Benjamin as he worked on his book during the warm summer months.

Meanwhile, the problems were continuing with L'Enfant. He was hard to work with and did not always agree with the President. Then one day, in an outburst of anger, L'Enfant left, taking all his plans for the new city with him.

So President Washington put Andrew Ellicott in charge of the plans. Now, along with the survey, Ellicott had to draw a new map of the city and select the places where the public buildings would be built.

On his trips back home, Ellicott often talked over his plans with Benjamin. "I want to copy as many of L'Enfant's ideas as possible, but I can recall only a few of them." Ellicott spoke in a defeated voice.

It is possible that Benjamin was able to help his friend remember some of L'Enfant's ideas. When Ellicott's map for the new city was finished, it was very much like the one L'Enfant had made.

The President was delighted with the map and with Mr. Ellicott's plans. So the capital city was finally built and was named Washington, after the first President of the United States.

Washington, D.C., proved to be as beautiful as everyone had hoped. This might not have happened without the careful planning of Andrew Ellicott and the fine work of Benjamin Banneker.

Stopping by Woods on a Snowy Evening

Whose woods these are I think I know.
His house is in the village, though;
He will not see me stopping here
To watch his woods fill up with snow.

My little horse must think it queer
To stop without a farmhouse near
Between the woods and frozen lake
The darkest evening of the year.

He gives his harness bells a shake
To ask if there is some mistake.
The only other sound's the sweep
Of easy wind and downy flake.

The woods are lovely, dark, and deep,
But I have promises to keep,
And miles to go before I sleep,
And miles to go before I sleep.

Robert Frost

SUGAR ON SNOW

"Sugar on snow,
Sugar on snow,
Pickles and doughnuts and
Sugar on snow!" Cammie
sang.

"What's sugar on snow?"
asked Kate.
"You'll see on my birthday!"
replied Cammie. And she started
singing again.

"Sugar on snow,
Sugar on snow,
Pickles and doughnuts and
Sugar on snow!"

206

"Today is the day to tap the trees," said Peter, sniffing the air. "Tomorrow we boil the sap."

"And the day after tomorrow is my birthday!" exclaimed Cammie. "I'll invite Mary, and Joe, and Mike, and Faith, and Betsy. Just think, a sugar-on-snow party for my birthday!"

"But there's no sugar," said Kate, "and there's no snow."

Peter laughed. "We're going to make the sugar. First we'll tap the trees. There's a nice, warm sun today, and tonight, unless I miss my guess, there'll be a freeze. That's perfect weather for sugar."

"But there's no snow!" repeated Kate.

The children climbed onto the wagon, taking along the spouts, and the pails, and the lids. They bounced along through the woods at an even pace, heading toward the grove of maple trees.

"Why didn't we sugar a week ago when there was snow?" asked Cammie, tugging at her brother's sleeve. "Then we could have had sugar on snow easily."

"We had no choice," explained Peter. "We can't just sugar whenever we want. We have to wait till spring, when the trees get warm and the sap begins to run."

"How do you know it isn't running if you don't even try?" asked Kate.

"Well, a farmer just knows. There's a different feel in the air. In wintertime the earth is frozen tight, the trees creak with cold, and the sap stays down in the roots."

He smiled at his younger sisters and continued, "Then one day it's sugaring time. The sun warms your face and the birds sing. Everything the sunlight touches kind of stretches and begins to feel alive again. That's when the sap rises in the maple trees. You have to catch the sap at just the right time—when it's cold from winter and sweet from spring."

The maple giants towered above, and the woods were peaceful. Only the clip-clop, clip-clop of the horses' hoofs broke the quiet. But when Peter stopped the wagon, the children could hear the birds singing and the sound of snow-cold water running in the brook.

Peter made a hole in the first maple tree and tapped in a spout. Then he stood back to watch. A bright, shiny drop of sap leaked out and landed on Kate's tongue. "Mmmm!" she said as she swallowed.

Cammie hung a pail under the spout, and Kate put on the lid. The sap began to drip, drop—drip, drop, drip into the pail. Sugaring had begun.

On through the grove they went, tapping other maple trees.

"We'll have sugar on snow for my birthday!" called Cammie.

"If it snows," replied Kate as she drank drop after drop of the sap.

The sun went down, and the shadows grew long. So the children climbed into the wagon and headed toward home.

Cammie's Good Luck

Next morning the children hitched Dick and Frosty to the wagon and went back to the woods. When they reached the first maple tree, Cammie jumped down and lifted a lid.

"The pail is full of sap!" she cried.

"OK. Let's pour it into the gathering tank in the back of the wagon," said Peter. "Don't spill any."

When all the pails were empty and hung back on the trees, Peter and Cammie and Kate drove home. Splish, splash, splosh! went the sap in the gathering tank.

The sap was hauled up to the sugarhouse, where it was poured into the sugar pan. Peter built a roaring fire, and the girls carried in wood, piles and piles and piles of wood.

The sap got warm. Then it got hot. Little bubbles danced in the bottom of the pan. The sap began to boil and jump, and steam curled up to the ceiling. It smelled like sugar, but it wasn't sugar just yet.

All afternoon the sap boiled and bubbled. Cammie drank some. It was thin and golden and sweet, but it wasn't syrup yet.

Kate tasted it and tasted it. The sap was hot and sticky, and it spilled down her snowsuit, and the spills tasted like sugar.

Inside, the sugarhouse smelled steamy and mapley, but it was cozy and warm. Outside, the night was clear and cold. The moon came out, and Mother let the children stay up late. The next day was Cammie's birthday, and they had to have the syrup for the sugar-on-snow party.

"The sap is ready," said Peter when it was very late. He turned the spout and out came the syrup, all finished.

"Syrup!" shouted Cammie. "Syrup for my sugar-on-snow party!"

"But there's still no snow," said Kate.

The next morning Cammie jumped out of bed and flew to the window. Would there be snow for her sugar-on-snow party?

"Happy birthday, Cammie!" shouted Peter.

"Snow!" yelled Cammie in delight.

A blanket of snow lay over the ground. White cupcakes of snow sat on every fence post. The bush by the kitchen door had powdery fingers of snow on every twig.

The barn and the sugarhouse had white snow-icing on their roofs, like birthday cakes.

The meadow was smooth and bright, just waiting for the first tracks to cut across its crust.

So everyone helped prepare for the party. Mother made fresh doughnuts and sprinkled them with sugar. Daddy brought home apple juice and big, sour pickles.

Down the road filed all of Cammie's friends—all racing for the sugarhouse.

Peter boiled the syrup until it was just right for sugar on snow. Cammie and Kate made a place in the clean snow, and Peter poured the syrup over it. The children watched excitedly as the hot syrup spilled onto the snow.

They waited for the syrup to become cold and waxy and chewy. Then they wound long strings of the waxlike sugar around forks and dropped the sugar into their open mouths.

Everyone drank apple juice and ate doughnuts sprinkled with powdered sugar. They chewed sour pickles to take away the sweet, and they ate sweet sugar to take away the sour.

When the party was over, Dick and Frosty took the children home. "Happy birthday, Cammie!" they shouted in gay voices. "Thank you for the sugar-on-snow party."

"Thank you for coming," answered Cammie.

And Kate added, "It's lucky it snowed."

How to Make
an Indian Design

Here are the things you need.

2 sticks, about 7" long
1 ball of yarn
White glue

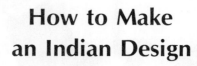

This is what you must do.

1. Cross the sticks in the center to make four arms.

2. Join the sticks together with glue. Press and put aside to dry.

3. When the glue is dry, wrap the yarn several times around the center, where the sticks cross.

4. Draw the yarn over and under Arm 1 until it has circled the stick.

5. Wrap Arm 2 in the same way—over, under, up, and around to Arm 3.

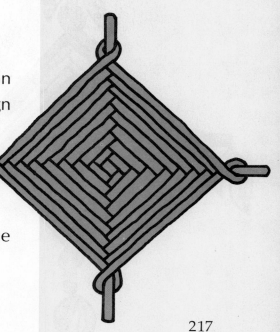

6. Continue to wrap each arm in the same way, until your design is the size you want.

7. Cut and knot the yarn in the back, where it will not show.

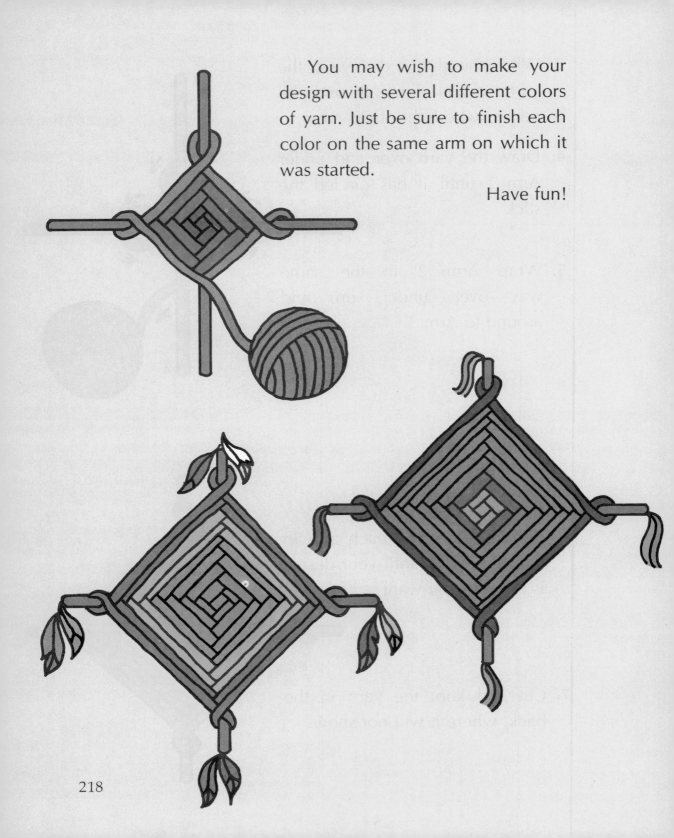

You may wish to make your design with several different colors of yarn. Just be sure to finish each color on the same arm on which it was started.

Have fun!

Bertram and His Giraffe

"I wonder what would happen if I had a giraffe," said Bertram.

"Giraffe? What put that crazy idea into your head?" asked his mother.

"Oh, I don't know," replied Bertram. "I was just wondering."

"Well, it might catch cold," his mother remarked, "and I would have to doctor it. As if I didn't have enough to do already!"

Then she changed the subject and went on making doughnuts. Bertram stood watching her as she cut out the lumps of dough and dropped them into the hot fat.

After a while he asked, "Mother, may I have one?"

Of course, his mother thought that Bertram wanted a doughnut. "You may have just one," she answered. "But don't tease for any more."

Bertram promised that he wouldn't.

Imagine her surprise, though, when he ran right out of the kitchen without even waiting for a doughnut! She supposed he had his mind on playing baseball with his friends.

But she was wrong. Bertram didn't have baseball on his mind at all. What he had on his mind was—a giraffe!

He hopped on his bike and rode as fast as he could to the place where giraffes were sold.

After asking the man how much the giraffe cost, Bertram selected a fancy one with green eyes and a curly tail. Then he bought a long piece of cord and tied it around the giraffe's neck. He hitched the other end of the cord to his bike and towed the giraffe home. Bertram put the giraffe in the cellar and named it Rudolph.

Bertram gave Rudolph an apple and tried to teach him to stand on his hind legs and beg.

But the giraffe said, "That's a crazy thing to ask me to do! I can't stand on my hind legs."

"Why not?"

"Because I'd bump my head on the ceiling."

So Bertram said, "I'll make a hole in it."

"No, don't!" exclaimed the giraffe quickly. "It might hurt."

"I mean the ceiling," explained Bertram. "I'll put the hole in the ceiling, not in your head."

So when Bertram had finished cutting the hole, he told Rudolph to poke his head through it. And Rudolph did.

"Now see if you can stand on your hind legs," said Bertram.

But Rudolph pulled his head out after a minute and said, "I can't do that. It's pitch dark up there, and I'm afraid of the dark."

"Oh," replied Bertram. "I guess that hole is in the floor of the hall closet where the raincoats are kept. Maybe I'd better make a little window in the door so you can look into the hallway."

But Rudolph didn't like that idea, either. "It's too stuffy in the hall closet," he explained. "Besides, there's not much of a view. Make me another hole."

So Bertram cut another hole, this time in the living-room floor. The giraffe stretched his neck through and smiled. "This is just perfect!" he exclaimed, enjoying the view.

That afternoon Bertram's little brother, Sam, was playing with a ball on the living-room floor. Rudolph's head wasn't sticking out of the hole, and the ball rolled in. Sam crept over to look for the ball, and he fell in, too. His heels caught on the very edge of the hole, and there he was, hanging upside down.

Bertram's mother heard Sam screaming. When she got to the living room, she didn't see him because only his heels were showing.

Finally she saw the hole and pulled Sam out. "Who made that hole?" she demanded in a loud voice.

"I did," answered Bertram.

"You might have known that your brother would be sure to fall through!" she said.

"I never thought about Sam when I made the hole," explained Bertram. "I made it for the giraffe."

"What giraffe?"

"My giraffe—the one you said I could have. His name is Rudolph."

"Oh," replied Bertram's mother. "That's a nice name."

Just then Rudolph poked his head through the hole. His long, thin neck looked like a snake and frightened Sam, who screamed louder than ever.

So Bertram's mother said, "Well, that giraffe can't go on scaring the baby like that. You'll just have to make another hole."

"But I've already made two holes!"

"Don't argue, Bertram. Do as I tell you."

So Bertram made another hole, this time in the bathroom floor. That night, when his mother was washing her face, the giraffe popped his head through the hole and nearly scared her out of her skin. She threw a cake of soap at him and stuffed up the hole with some towels.

Then she laid down the law.

"See here, Bertram!" she cried. "I don't intend to have that wild animal staring at me. You'll have to put the giraffe somewhere else."

Bertram knew she meant business, so he got Rudolph and moved him into his bedroom. Then he cut a hole in the ceiling so the giraffe could stick his head into the attic.

But it was chilly in the attic, and Rudolph caught a terrible cold. His throat was sore all the way down. When he coughed, he made a strange sound—"Ark, ark, ark!"

Bertram's mother heard the coughing and thought Bertram must be sick. She hurried into his bedroom and stuck a cough drop in his mouth.

Rudolph kept on coughing, and Bertram kept getting cough drops stuck in his mouth. He didn't have a chance to explain because his mother wouldn't let him talk.

The next night, before Bertram went to bed, she rubbed goose grease all over his chest and made him soak his feet in hot water.

"This should fix your cold," she said.

"But I don't have a . . ." It was no use. Bertram's mother told him to keep still so his throat wouldn't get worse. And all night long the coughing continued—"Ark, ark, ark!"

Finally Bertram's mother called the doctor. "I've rubbed Bertram's chest with goose grease," she said, "and given him no end of cough drops. He's soaked his feet in hot water, yet he still coughs his head off. You'd better come over."

"That's funny," said the doctor after he had checked Bertram. "There doesn't appear to be a thing wrong with this boy."

But Bertram's mother said, "Cough, dear."

So Bertram coughed. "Ka-ha! Ka-ha! Ka-ha!"

"Not that way. Cough like you did last night—'Ark, ark, ark!'"

"But I didn't cough," said Bertram. "That was my giraffe, Rudolph."

"I might have known," sighed his mother. Then she asked the doctor to help Rudolph, but this made the doctor angry.

"I'm not a giraffe doctor!" he shouted, and he hurried out the door.

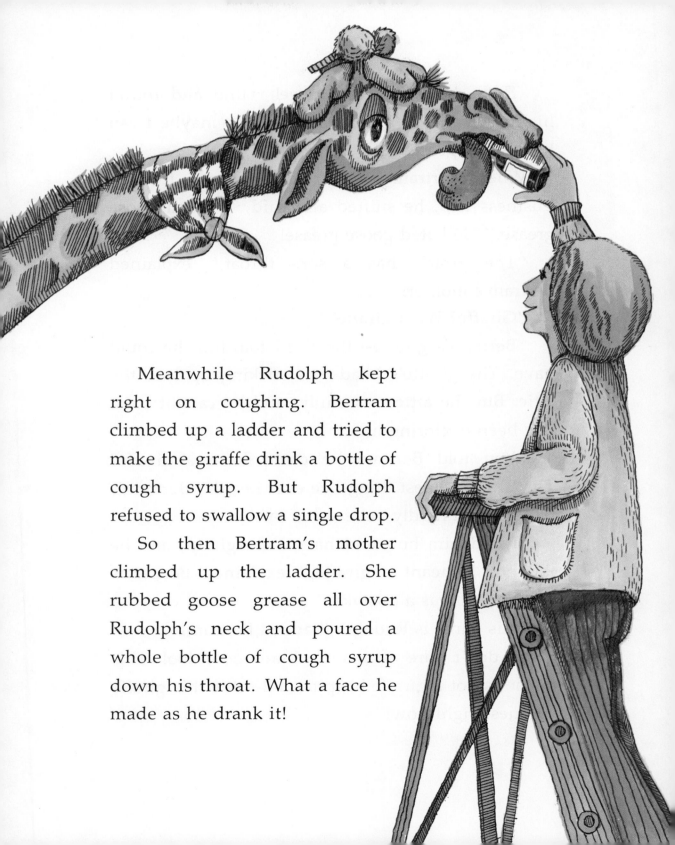

Meanwhile Rudolph kept right on coughing. Bertram climbed up a ladder and tried to make the giraffe drink a bottle of cough syrup. But Rudolph refused to swallow a single drop.

So then Bertram's mother climbed up the ladder. She rubbed goose grease all over Rudolph's neck and poured a whole bottle of cough syrup down his throat. What a face he made as he drank it!

Then she wrapped a towel round and round his neck and put him to bed. "Now, maybe I can have some peace," she said.

When Bertram's father came home from a business trip, he sniffed and said, "I smell goose grease." He hated goose grease!

"The giraffe has a sore throat," explained Bertram's mother.

"Giraffe? What giraffe?"

"Bertram's giraffe—the one I told him he could have. The giraffe's head was sticking up into the attic. But the attic was chilly, and he caught cold. I've been doctoring him."

"You told Bertram he could have a giraffe? That's the craziest thing I've ever heard." Bertram's father could hardly believe his ears.

"I told him he could have a doughnut, and he thought I meant a giraffe," explained Bertram's mother. "It was a mistake."

"His name is Rudolph," added Bertram.

"I don't care if it's Cock-a-doodle-doo! This house is not a giraffe hospital. I'll settle this giraffe business right now!"

So he bundled Rudolph into a cart, with his neck and legs sticking straight up into the air, and wheeled him over to the zoo.

The zoo keeper put Rudolph in a nice, tall cage next to a hippo. All the schoolchildren came and gave Rudolph apples, but he never did learn to stand on his hind legs and beg.

After that, when Bertram asked for anything, his mother made sure she knew what he wanted. And she never had to doctor a giraffe again.

Two Witches

There was a witch
The witch had an itch
The itch was so itchy it
Gave her a twitch.

Another witch
Admired the twitch
So she started twitching
Though she had no itch.

Now both of them twitch
So it's hard to tell which
Witch has the itch and
Which witch has the twitch.

Alexander Resnikoff

233

A Pair of Problems

There is a mill with seven corners.
In each corner stand seven bags.
Upon each bag sit seven cats.
Each cat has seven kittens.
When the miller and his wife come into the mill,
how many feet will there be in the mill?

Answer

Four. The cats have paws.

A man with a fox, a goose, and some corn wanted to cross a river. He could take only one thing across at a time. If he left the goose and the corn while he took the fox over, the goose would eat the corn. If he left the fox and the goose while he took the corn over, the fox would kill the goose. How did the man get over the river?

Answer

First he took the goose over. He came back and took the fox over. Then he brought the goose back. He left the goose and took the corn over. Then he returned and took the goose over again.

Adventures of Paul Bunyan

Some folks say he was born near the coast of Maine. Some say he came out of the woods of Canada. But they all agree that his name was Paul Bunyan and that he was the hero of the Northwest. And they also agree that Paul grew up to be the biggest person in the whole country.

How big was he?

Well, the folks that live along the coast of Maine say that when Paul was born, he outgrew his cradle before he was a week old.

"What will we do?" asked Paul's mother. "This cradle has always been big enough for the other children."

"Can't you starve him a little?" questioned his father. "The way Paul goes after food, he'll eat us out of house and home—and then eat the house, too!"

"Don't be silly," said his mother, whose name was Jane and who considered herself very wise. "A growing child has to grow. That's what he's here for."

"Well," grumbled Paul's father, whose name was Habakkuk, "I don't see what you expect me to do when I've got a thousand things—"

"I expect you to stop dragging your muddy boots all over my clean kitchen and get out your tools and build a bigger cradle," said Paul's mother. And she began mopping up the boot tracks from the floor to show her husband there was no time to waste.

So Paul's father took down his hammer and saw. He carved and chipped and pounded away until he made something that looked a little like a box and a little like a boat. It was six feet long, and it took him about a week to make. But it didn't help. By the time the cradle was finished, Paul had grown too big to fit it.

"All that work for nothing," groaned Habakkuk as he paced back and forth. "Now I'll have to build another cradle."

There were some woods behind the house, and Paul's father cut down a tree that was twelve feet high. He hollowed it out and smoothed the sides until they shone like moonlight on silver.

But by the time the new cradle was ready, Paul had gained over a hundred pounds and was nearly fourteen feet long.

"Well," said Habakkuk, refusing to accept defeat, "I'll see if I can't build faster than Paul can grow."

This time Habakkuk didn't stop to do any fine chipping or carving. He didn't smooth or polish or try anything fancy. He just took some boards that were twenty feet long and hammered them together to form a long, narrow box. And Paul fitted it to the last quarter of an inch.

But Paul's father had forgotten to put on the rockers. And how are you going to get a baby—even a twenty-foot baby—to close his eyes unless he can rock himself to sleep?

"This is a new kind of cradle," Habakkuk said, pretending he had made it that way on purpose. "It's a floating cradle. We'll put it in the ocean, and the waves will rock Paul to sleep."

Habakkuk and Jane tied one end of a heavy cord to the cradle and the other end of the cord to the pier. Then they put the cradle in the water. But Paul was restless. He rocked and rocked—and by midnight there was a huge wave that wiped out half of the villages along the coast of Maine.

That was the beginning of the trouble. Maine folks don't anger easily, but when they get mad, their shouts are worse than the rumble of thunder. But now they were helpless. They couldn't put Paul in jail, for he was just a baby. Besides, there wasn't any jail big enough to hold him. They looked in the law books, but there was nothing against anyone being twenty feet tall. And there certainly was no law saying a person must stop growing.

While the folks were trying to decide what to do, Paul's mother rushed out of the house.

"It's gone!" she cried, wringing her hands.

"What's gone?" asked one of the townspeople.

"The box—the boat—the floating cradle—whatever you call it. And Paul with it. I looked out of the window, and I couldn't believe my eyes. What do you think I saw?"

"Come to the point, Jane. What did you see?"

"Paul got out of the cradle—don't ask me how! And then he picked it up. And then he walked to shore. And then"—she drew a deep breath—"then he disappeared."

"That's just like Paul," said Habakkuk, suddenly proud of his son. "The little fellow was different from the very beginning. Yes, sir, he's going places—going far."

Habakkuk was right. The next time they heard of Paul, he had gone far. He was away out in Minnesota.

Paul Meets His Match

Stories about Paul Bunyan began to float back East. He was still growing and doing surprising things. He had been seen lifting horses across a river. He had built a house in Minnesota, a house so high that the last five stories had to be put on springs to let the moon pass by.

This was the country for Paul. Huge trees grew from the Great Lakes clear through Minnesota and for thousands of miles on to the West Coast. There were trees so wide a man would get tired walking around their trunks, trees so high that people would need days to find their tops.

But the huge trees didn't stop Paul! He took to the woods as though he were born there. He became a lumberjack and could bring the biggest trees crashing to the ground with his mighty ax.

Paul had been a lumberjack for only a short time when he met up with six men. "You're the best lumberjack of all time!" they cried when they saw how Paul could swing an ax. "We'll work for you and make the other lumberjacks look as if they're cutting corn instead of trees."

So with Paul as their leader, the men became the greatest logging outfit that ever went into the woods.

The second winter was the coldest winter the world had ever known. The men turned blue from the cold. Their lips, their fingertips, their toes, their noses—everything about them turned blue. Then it began to snow. And the snow was blue! For forty days and forty nights the blue stuff kept falling, stretching across the whole Northwest.

"There must be an end of it," said Paul one ice-blue morning. "I'm going out and search."

So he left the woods, cleared a few rivers, climbed over a mountain, and there he was on the coast of the greatest of all lakes. Ice cakes were tossing about on the freezing waves, pounding against each other and hammering the shore.

One huge wave of white water lifted itself above the others, and there, among the ice cakes, Paul saw two ears. Nothing of the rest of the creature could be seen—just two, huge ears. Then they disappeared.

Paul pulled up his boots and headed into the icy waters. The waves roared and the ice pounded, but there was no sign of life in the huge lake. Just as he was about to turn back, the two ears appeared again. Paul leaned over and caught hold of them. He dragged them toward the shore, and as he pulled them out of the water, a head came into view. Then came a pair of shoulders, two front legs, a thin body, two hind legs, and a water-soaked tail. The creature was less than half alive, and all his body was sky blue.

"Well," said Paul, "if there can be blue snow, I suppose there can be a blue calf. Or maybe he's just blue with the cold."

But when Paul worked over the calf's body and rubbed him and warmed him in front of the fire, the calf did not change color. If anything, the color became a brighter blue. Paul had some milk with him, and he poured it down the calf's throat. The animal didn't open his eyes, but he gave the first sign of life. The calf licked Paul's face as he bent over.

"What a baby!" said Paul. "If he lives, that's what I'll call him—Babe, the Blue Ox."

In the morning Babe's eyes were wide open, and his tongue was hanging out. "He might die from hunger—and my supply of milk is gone. I don't suppose he will touch my hot cakes and coffee. Now that he's living, it'd be a shame to let him starve."

But Babe ate up the hot cakes, drank the coffee, and, still hungry, took a big bite out of the coffeepot.

"You're quite a calf!" said Paul.

As though in answer, Babe struggled to his feet, lowered his head, and kicked Paul from behind. Paul was thrown ten feet in the air and came down like a load of rocks.

"You're a little wonder!" exclaimed Paul, getting to his feet and rubbing the snow out of his eyes. "You're certainly the ox for me. But I don't dare take you back to the logging camp—not quite yet."

So he began feeding Babe. He tried every kind of food he could find. But at the end of every dinner, Babe was still hungry.

One day after the ox had lapped up ten bowls of soup, Paul went out to get some food for himself. When he returned, Babe had eaten most of Paul's blankets and was chewing what was left of the pots and pans.

"Babe!" shouted Paul, with a sour look on his face.

The ox tried to look sorry. He wanted to win back Paul's friendship with a weak moo. But what came out was a loud roar, a roar that shook the hills and knocked against the sky.

"That settles it," said Paul. "We're wasting time. If you're big enough to roar like that, you're big enough to work. Now, let's see if you can get to camp under your own power."

So they set out for the logging camp. The farther they walked, the bigger Babe grew. By the time they reached camp, the ox was as big as Paul. He stood as though carved out of blue stone, a giant among giants.

"Forty-two hammer lengths between the eyes!" cried one of the lumberjacks. "But there's no telling how much he weighs."

"What are you going to do with him?" asked another.

"Do? Just you wait and see," said Paul. "Just wait until he gets all his growth."

Babe was full-grown by the end of the winter. The last of the blue snow had melted, but Babe was bluer than ever—bluer and bigger.

People said Babe had such a long body they couldn't get a full view of him at one time. They said Paul had to carry a pair of field glasses so he could see what the Blue Ox was doing with his hind feet. But that was stretching the truth. Paul knew what to do with Babe all right, and, for all his size, the Blue Ox followed Paul around like a puppy.

There was no job too hard for Babe. He could haul anything anywhere. Whenever Paul decided to move to better logging grounds, the whole camp would be hitched to Babe. The Blue Ox would take a deep breath and drag the camp, kitchen and all, behind him.

253

Perhaps Babe's hardest task was working on the roads near the camp. The problem wasn't that the roads were so narrow but that they were so crooked. Some roads were so crooked that they doubled back on each other, and the men would meet themselves coming back from work. But Paul fixed that. He tied one end of a heavy cord to Babe and the other end to the crooked road. Then he yelled, "Pull, Babe, pul-l-l-l!"

And by the end of the following winter, Babe had straightened out every crooked road.

Today the logging country isn't what it was in Paul's day. The machines have come in and cleared much of the land. Paul would have a hard time finding the right sort of place to swing his ax. But folks still talk of what he did when the woods were wild and young. Perhaps he still calls Babe and walks with him across the mountains. Perhaps it's Paul's voice that is sometimes heard on a cold winter day, "Pull, Babe, pul-l-l-l!" One thing is certain—you won't hear the last of Paul Bunyan and his Blue Ox until the very last tree in every forest is down.

What Can It Be?

1. It is neither in the house
   Nor out of the house,
   But it is part of the house.

2. It has four legs, but it can't walk.
   It has a head, but it can't talk.

3. It belongs to you,
   But others use it more than you do.

4. You use it between your head and your toes.
   The more you use it, the thinner it grows.

5. It runs up the hill
   And down the hill,
   But it always stands still.

Answers

5. A road
4. A bar of soap
3. Your name
2. A bed
1. A window

255

The Man Who Didn't Wash His Dishes

There was once a man who lived all alone in a little house at the edge of town. He didn't have a wife or any children, so he always cooked his own supper, cleaned his own house, and made his own bed. One night he came home hungrier than ever, so he made himself a big supper of roast beef and vegetables. It was a good supper, but he ate so much roast beef that he grew very tired.

After he'd finished, he sat back, as full as he could be, and decided to leave the dishes till the next night. Then he would wash them all at one time.

But the next night the man was twice as hungry, so he cooked twice as big a supper. He took twice as long to eat it and was twice as tired by the time he'd finished. So he left those dishes in the sink, too.

Well, as the days went by, the man got hungrier and hungrier, and more and more tired, and he never washed his dishes. After a while there were so many dirty dishes that they didn't fit in the sink, and he began to pile them on the table.

Soon the table was full, and the man began to put the dishes in his bookcase. And when the bookcase was full, he put the dishes wherever he could find an empty place. Before long he even had them piled on the floor. In fact, the floor got to be so full of dishes that the man had a hard time getting into his house at night.

Then one day he discovered that he hadn't a clean dish left. He was hungry enough to eat out of anything, so he ate out of the soap dish from the bathroom. He couldn't use that again, so he used ashtrays. When he ran out of ashtrays, he got some clean flowerpots from the cellar.

Finally there was nothing left to eat from but the candy dishes. He had used everything—even the pots and pans that he cooked his food in. The whole house was full of dirty dishes, dirty ashtrays, dirty flowerpots, dirty candy dishes, dirty pots and pans, and one dirty soap dish. He couldn't find his books or his alarm clock or even his bed! He couldn't sit down to think because the chairs were filled with dishes, and he couldn't find the sink in order to wash them.

All of a sudden it began to rain, and the man got an idea. He drove his big truck around to the side of the house. Then he piled all the dishes, all the ashtrays, all the flowerpots, all the candy dishes, all the pots and pans, and the one soap dish onto the truck. He drove it out into the middle of the yard. The rain fell on everything, and soon everything was clean again.

So the man carried the things back into the house. He put the dishes in the cupboard, along with the pots and pans. He put the ashtrays on the tables, the candy dishes on the shelf, the flowerpots in the cellar, and the soap dish in the bathroom.

He was hungry after all that work. So once again he made himself a big supper of roast beef and vegetables. It was a good supper, but he ate so much roast beef that he grew very tired. After he'd finished, he sat back, as full as he could be, and decided to leave the dishes till the next night.

And if you remember how this tale began, you will know exactly what happened after that!

Book-length Story

The Turnabout Trick

"I've talked with Fenton's mother," said Mrs. Maxwell, "and we agree that you can have a cookout and then sleep in your clubhouse tonight."

"Great!" said Kerby Maxwell.

"Good!" said Fenton Claypool.

Waldo leaped up to lick Mrs. Maxwell's hand, then sat down happily beside the boys, polishing the kitchen floor with his bushy tail. Waldo loved to eat hot dogs when they were roasted over a campfire.

"Of course, if you make any trouble for Mrs. Pembroke, or anybody else, that will be the end of the clubhouse," warned Kerby's mother. "But I'm sure you won't. After all, you didn't get into any trouble the first time you slept out."

Oh, no? Fenton and Kerby glanced at one another and then at Waldo, who nibbled the fur on his right paw and pretended he had not been listening.

But a few minutes later, when the three of them were alone in the backyard, Waldo had to listen to a warning from his master. "None of your disappearing tricks!" ordered Kerby.

He checked to be sure the dog was wearing his collar. Last time Waldo had gone away without it, and the boys had spent the whole evening looking for him.

"If things go OK tonight, we may get to sleep out whenever we want," remarked Fenton.

At that very moment Mr. and Mrs. Maxwell came out of their house. "You know where to phone us if you need anything," called Kerby's father, getting into the car. "We won't be late."

Kerby and Fenton nodded and watched the Maxwells leave.

While the boys were trying to decide how soon they should start the campfire, Mrs. Pembroke came out of the house next door. She walked down the front steps and got into a car with three other ladies. They were on the way to their usual Friday night dinner party, after which they would play bridge at Mrs. Pembroke's house.

The boys could see the card table, with the candy dishes and nut cups, all set up in her living room. In about two hours the women would return, and the fun would begin. Their idea of fun, anyway.

Mrs. Pembroke was always yelling about little things, like when Kerby and Waldo were in a hurry and cut across a corner of her lawn. Or when Waldo caught her old cat Xerxes outside and chased him up a tree.

"What do you know!" said Fenton as he watched the car disappear down the street. "Mrs. Pembroke was in such a hurry to leave that she forgot to turn off her basement light."

"She left a window open, too," noticed Kerby, glancing in the same direction.

"Hey, look!" cried Fenton.

A large head covered with yellow fur poked out of the basement window and then disappeared.

"It's Xerxes! He's trying to get out the window!" exclaimed Kerby.

"Maybe we ought to close the window, Kerby," said Fenton.

But Kerby just grinned. "We can't do that. Mrs. Pembroke has said we're not to set foot on her lawn again. Goodness me, we must be good boys and obey Mrs. Pembroke!"

"By all means," agreed Fenton in a high voice, suddenly grinning, too.

As they talked, the big cat's head appeared again, his claws trying to grab hold of something. Then he dropped out of sight.

"Aw, I don't think he can make it," said Kerby.

Xerxes must have heard Kerby and decided to show him what a big yellow cat could do. The cat's head shot into sight once more, and this time, slowly but surely, he pulled himself up and out.

Stopping to catch his breath, Xerxes sat down to wash his paws and give his face a quick once-over.

Now that the cat was outside, Kerby did the only thing he could possibly do at such a time.

"Sic 'em!" he said to Waldo.

With a glad bark Waldo raced through the hedge. Xerxes took one look and headed for a tree, with Waldo close behind. The cat shot up the tree as usual and grabbed a small branch about fourteen feet above the ground.

Xerxes had grabbed that branch a hundred times before. Who would have thought it would ever break?

But it did, and without warning, down came Xerxes, branch and all.

Whether the branch hit the cat on the head or he landed on his head, nobody could be sure. But the fact remained, Xerxes did not manage to make a catlike landing on his feet. Instead there he lay, stretched out on the lawn.

Waldo sniffed around and looked up at the boys with a worried whine. The last thing he wanted was to catch Xerxes. Cats were for chasing, not catching. After all, a dog would soon run out of cats if he went around catching them! Waldo loved simply to chase Xerxes. And Xerxes loved to be chased so he could show everyone how good he was at climbing trees. It was a good deal that kept everybody happy, except Mrs. Pembroke, who didn't understand and never would.

Both boys raced through the hedge. Waldo was whining worse than ever.

"Oh, brother!" groaned Kerby as they bent over the lifeless cat. "Come on, Xerxes, wake up! Jumping jeepers! What if he's dead?"

The thought was a terrible one. What would Mrs. Pembroke do?

"She'll think we killed Xerxes!"

But just when they were beginning to feel very sorry for themselves, the big cat moved.

Waldo, who had his nose right over Xerxes, jumped back a foot.

Xerxes moved again. Then his whole body stirred. His eyes opened.

"Xerxes! Are you all right?"

The cat got to his feet and shook his head sharply.

"He's OK!"

Kerby took hold of Waldo's collar to keep him back until they knew what Xerxes would do.

But the cat's eyes did not narrow, and he didn't hiss or spit. He didn't even swish his tail. Instead he began to move it in a very strange way.

There was only one way to describe it. Instead of swishing his tail, Xerxes was wagging it.

Putting his head down playfully between his paws, Xerxes made a noise that sounded like "Br-r-row-row!" Suddenly he began jumping, puppylike, around Waldo.

Xerxes wanted to play!

If a dog could turn red, Waldo would have been that dog. He walked away stiffly, but Xerxes was right there, running along after Waldo.

"Jeepers! Je-e-e-eepers!"

The boys stared at each other as the awful truth hit them.

"Xerxes thinks he's a dog!"

In the Doghouse

The awful truth must have hit Waldo, too, and he was trying to escape as fast as he could. He ran this way and that, whining and trying to find a place to hide.

"Amnesia! That's what's the matter. Xerxes has amnesia," decided Fenton.

"Amnesia? What's that?" questioned Kerby.

"It's when a person gets hit on the head and forgets things. Xerxes has forgotten he's a cat."

"Forgetting he's a cat is one thing," said Kerby, "but to wake up and think he's a dog—!"

"I guess that is a little unusual," agreed Fenton. "It's very interesting though. I don't suppose many people have ever had a chance to see a cat who thought he was a dog."

"No, I guess not, and I wish someone else had this chance instead of us," Kerby grumbled worriedly. "What's going to happen when Mrs. Pembroke comes home and Xerxes barks at her?"

The boys stared at each other. Then they broke into broad grins. Come to think of it, that might not be so bad!

"Well, how about Waldo?" Kerby went on. "He's going to have a fit if this keeps up."

By now Waldo was on the back porch, demanding to be let in. He was ready to spend the rest of his days hiding rather than playing with a mixed-up cat.

"Before we do anything else, we ought to run a few tests to make sure of Xerxes' condition." Fenton picked up a small stick and called, "Here, Xerxes! Here, boy!"

Xerxes glanced around and looked pleased. He came running over excitedly.

"Go get it, boy!" cried Fenton as he tossed the stick over the cat's head.

Whirling around, Xerxes was after the stick in a flash, snapping it up almost before it had reached the ground. He returned with the stick, laid it at Fenton's feet, and stood back wagging his tail.

"He certainly passed that test," said Fenton. "Let's see, now, what else?"

He snapped his fingers as he thought of another idea. "I know. Kerby, will you bring me one of those puppy biscuits of Waldo's?"

"Sure!"

Kerby got the idea at once. He went into the kitchen, took down the puppy-biscuit box from the cupboard, and hurried outside with it.

Imagine how Waldo felt when he saw Kerby stoop down and hold out a biscuit to a cat!

Wagging his tail, Xerxes sniffed the biscuit. Then he took it in his mouth, turned, and walked away with it, just as if he were carrying a real bone.

"Let's follow him!" whispered Kerby.

"Yes, but not too close," replied Fenton as he held out his arm. "Grab Waldo."

There was no need to hold back Waldo. He didn't plan to get any closer to Xerxes than he had to. Together the three of them followed the big cat through the hedge and into his own backyard.

"What's he going to do?" asked Kerby.

"Who knows?"

Xerxes answered the question for them. Dropping the biscuit on the ground, he began to dig a hole.

The boys couldn't believe their eyes.

"He's going to bury it!" They shook their heads slowly at each other.

"No question about it," cried Fenton. "He really thinks he's a dog!"

They watched Waldo stare at Xerxes, then turn and walk away on four of the weakest legs any dog ever had.

"We've got to do something," said Kerby. "I don't think Waldo can take much more of this."

Perhaps it was the time of day—that mysterious time when the setting sun makes everything seem unreal—that made Kerby think of their friend, Mrs. Graymalkin. It was exactly her time of day, too. Just the time when they were certain to find her in the park, taking a walk.

Kerby had first met her there at this time of day. The high heel of her shoe had got stuck in a crack in the sidewalk, and he had worked it loose. The next day she had given him an old chemistry set that had belonged to her son.

Quite a few strange things had happened whenever Kerby used the chemistry set. The fact remained, however, that it was Mrs. Graymalkin who had helped the boys the night Waldo disappeared—the first time they were allowed to have a cookout. And here they were, hoping to have another cookout, and in trouble again.

"Let's go see if we can find Mrs. Graymalkin," said Kerby. Fenton agreed so quickly that Kerby knew he must have had the same idea.

"What can we do with Xerxes while we're gone?" asked Fenton.

"Say, that's right! We can't leave him running around loose, acting like a dog."

Kerby's glance fell on the doghouse beside the garage. "Why don't we put him in Waldo's doghouse? He'll be OK there."

"No, it won't work," replied Fenton. "Xerxes would be able to climb over that wire fence in nothing flat."

"Not if he thinks he's a dog!"

"Say, maybe you're right!" exclaimed Fenton. "But what if Mrs. Pembroke should come home early? If she did, and found Xerxes locked in the pen, acting like a dog . . .!"

Kerby nodded. It was painful even to imagine what would happen. But the boys didn't have any other choice.

Fenton picked up the stick again.

"Here, boy! Catch!" he cried, throwing the stick over the fence and into the pen. Xerxes raced after the stick.

"Close the gate!"

Kerby slammed it shut. Trapped inside, Xerxes
stood on his hind legs against the fence, dancing
up and down and giving out what sounded like a
puppy's whine. It was almost worse than his bark.
Waldo all but put his paws over his ears.

And sure enough, Xerxes didn't try to climb the
fence.

"You're right, Kerby! Xerxes doesn't think he
can climb it!"

"Good. Now, let's head for the park!"

Hurrying along a tree-lined path leading into the park, the boys searched for Mrs. Graymalkin. And suddenly there she was, walking around a bend in the path. When she saw them coming, her face lighted up with her usual smile.

"Well, well, well! Kerby and Fenton, and dear little Waldo! How nice to see you all again."

"Hello, Mrs. Graymalkin," said Kerby, trying to sound cheerful.

"Tell me now, what is your problem?" asked the old lady.

Kerby was surprised. "How did you know we have one?"

Mrs. Graymalkin's laugh sounded like that of a trained crow with a heavy cold. "It's written all over your faces, as usual. Even dear little Waldo looks worried."

"Well, he should be. He's the one with the most worries," said Kerby, and he told her what had happened.

"My, my, my! That's one of the most interesting cases of amnesia I've ever heard of!"

"I told you it was amnesia, Kerby!"

"A cat suffering from amnesia thinks it's something else," explained Mrs. Graymalkin. "Usually it thinks it's a dog, though there was one case when a cat thought it was a mouse. Such a pitiful case."

"You mean you've heard of other cases like Xerxes'?" asked Kerby.

"Oh, my, indeed I have. I happen to have made quite a study of cats. Yes, indeed," replied Mrs. Graymalkin with a laugh that made her sound exactly like a witch.

Fenton had said there were no such things as witches, but Kerby wasn't so sure. Anyway, even if Mrs. Graymalkin was a witch, she was a good one and nothing to be afraid of.

"Amnesia. Well, well, well. Let me see now, what shall we do about that?" Already Mrs. Graymalkin had laid a long, bony finger alongside her long, bony nose, and her eyes rolled up in thought.

Kerby knew what she was going to ask even before she asked it. "Yes, Mrs. Graymalkin," he said. "I've still got my chemistry set hidden away where my mother won't find it and get excited."

"Kerby! You're getting to be a mind reader," she replied with another of her witchlike laughs. "Well, now, remember this. Three from the right and three from the left, six from the right and four from the left, six and four together, and stir, stir, stir! Let's hear you repeat that, boys."

Together they repeated the words.

"Now, what do you think that means?"

They looked at each other. "Well," said Kerby, "the third tube from the right and the third tube from the left—"

"Good, good, good!"

"Six drops from the right tube and four drops from the left," added Fenton.

"Wonderful! You boys are growing smarter and smarter every day! Mix together, and stir, stir, stir. Then do as I tell you," said Mrs. Graymalkin, and she explained what they were to do. "And now I must be on my way!"

"Thanks a lot, Mrs. Graymalkin," called the boys as they watched her disappear round the bend in the path.

"Hey, Fenton," said Kerby in a strange voice, "are you sure Mrs. Graymalkin's not a w—?"

"Sure I'm sure! If there were such things, and she was one, she wouldn't need a chemistry set."

Kerby sighed. "That's what I thought. She'd just say some magic words."

"Right," said Fenton, and he sighed, too.

Crazy Mix-up

The boys could hear Xerxes whining the moment they reached the front lawn.

"Take it easy, Xerxes," said Kerby as they rounded the side of the house. "We'll have you back up a tree in no time."

Once in the basement Kerby hurriedly took his chemistry set from its hiding place.

The chemistry set had seen quite a bit of service since Mrs. Graymalkin had given it to him. Several of the glass tubes had been used up and thrown away. But the third tube from the right and the third from the left were still in their places. The right-hand tube was half full of a pale orange liquid. The left-hand tube had a small amount of colorless liquid.

Kerby went to work while Fenton watched closely. Six drops from the third tube from the right, four drops from the third tube from the left. Stir, stir, stir.

Kerby held up the mixture, and both boys looked it over carefully.

"Let's go get a puppy biscuit," said Kerby. "We'll brush this stuff all over it and feed it to Xerxes!"

When they went outside, Xerxes started up the puppy whine again.

"OK, come out and play," said Kerby as he opened the door of the pen.

The big cat came dashing out and looked around, wagging his bushy tail.

"He makes a pretty good puppy," remarked Fenton. "I mean, for a cat he's not bad at all."

Listening to such foolishness was too much for Waldo. Sticking his head over the edge of the porch, he barked at Xerxes so loudly that the poor cat fell off the step trying to get away.

"Cut that out, Waldo! Never mind him, Xerxes. Here's a nice bone for you." Kerby stooped to hand the cat the bone-shaped puppy biscuit brushed with the liquid.

When Waldo saw that happen, he jumped into the air as if he had been sitting on a bee. He was so mad that if he had known how, he would have packed up his rug and his food dish and left home.

Xerxes sniffed the bone and then took it in his mouth. "Attaboy! Eat the nice bone!" said Kerby.

But Xerxes had turned around and was walking toward the hedge again.

"Don't tell me . . ." groaned Fenton.

"Not again!" exclaimed Kerby.

Somehow Xerxes had got the idea that the only thing dogs ever did with bones was bury them. Because once again that was what he did.

"We'll never get anywhere with a bone-shaped biscuit," decided Fenton. "What we have to do is break off a piece and soak it in the stuff. Then Xerxes will eat it, and we'll be all set."

"I'll bet you're right, Fenton. Let's try it. First we'd better get Xerxes back in the pen. And let's make it snappy."

Back in the basement Kerby got out the chemistry set, and Fenton sat down on a box to think. "I'm sure this plan will work," he said. "We were just going at things wrong."

"Where's Waldo?" asked Kerby, suddenly realizing that Waldo was nowhere to be seen.

"I guess he went outside. Come to think of it, I heard the screen door slam a minute ago."

"We'd better find him."

Upstairs the kitchen was empty. They walked onto the back porch and called, "Here, Waldo! Come on boy!"

"Hey, look, Kerby. Waldo is over in Mrs. Pembroke's yard."

"What's he doing over there?"

"Say, what is he doing?"

"I think he's dug up something," said Kerby.

Jumping off the porch, Fenton led the way through the hedge. And there was Waldo, sitting under a tree beside a freshly dug hole.

"How do you like that? He's dug up Xerxes's biscuits!"

"I'll bet he was mad because you gave them to Xerxes, so now he's dug them up and has eaten them!"

"Crazy dog!" said Kerby. "Waldo, come here this minute!"

Waldo looked around at them, and his tail began to swish back and forth.

"Meow?" said Waldo.

For a moment Fenton thought Kerby was going to pass out. Mrs. Pembroke's cat was one thing. His dog was another. And to have one's very own dog start swishing his tail around and meowing was more than any red-blooded American boy could take.

"Waldo! Cut it out! Fun's fun, but if this is your idea of a joke, it's not funny!" Kerby shouted as Waldo, having eaten, sat down and began washing his face with one paw.

"Easy, Kerby! Waldo can't help it. He ate that puppy biscuit with the mixture on it, and the stuff worked."

"Worked? You call this working?"

"The mixture was supposed to make Xerxes think he was a cat. So when Waldo ate it . . ."

Once he realized what had happened, Kerby fell into a heap on the ground. Luckily Fenton kept his head.

"Listen, Kerby, now we need Mrs. Graymalkin more than ever!"

Kerby raised his head and stared at his friend. "Boy, did you ever say a mouthful!"

"Then come on. We've got to get going!"

Kerby struggled to his feet. By promising Waldo a nice bowl of milk, the boys managed to get him back to the house. He spit at Xerxes only once on the way, when the cat barked at him.

In the kitchen they poured milk into Waldo's food dish and left him meowing happily over it.

"We're getting nowhere faster than anybody else ever got nowhere before!" groaned Kerby while they hurried as fast as they could toward the park. "Now we not only have a cat who thinks he's a dog, we have a dog who thinks he's a cat!"

"Don't worry, Kerby," said Fenton, trying to sound sure of himself. "Mrs. Graymalkin will work out something."

"I hope you're right. But every time we use that chemistry set, we seem to end up with the wrong trick and more trouble!"

"Well, you can't blame this one on her!"

Fenton pointed ahead, "Look, we're just in time! There she is, getting into her car! Hey, Mrs. Graymalkin!"

"Well, well, well! Kerby and Fenton again!" she said. "Where is dear little Waldo? And the cat —what's his name again?"

"Xerxes, and he's still barking. Waldo ate the biscuit with the stuff on it, and he's home meowing. Waldo thinks he's a cat!"

For a single instant Mrs. Graymalkin stared at the boys. Then she threw back her head and let loose with the wildest laugh anybody had ever heard. "Oh, my, oh, my! That's the best laugh I've had for days. Dear little Waldo acting like a kitty." She wiped the tears from her eyes. "Well now, this problem will have to be solved another way." Her beady eyes looked right at Kerby. "When you get home, this is what you must do . . ."

Kerby listened, but when she had finished, a groan escaped him.

"That's swell, Mrs. Graymalkin—but if Mrs. Pembroke is home, nothing's going to help!"

"What do you mean by that, Kerby?"

After he had explained, Mrs. Graymalkin said, "Why didn't you tell me? Hop into my car, and I'll drive you home."

A Race Against Time

In no time at all, the car rounded the street corner where Kerby lived.

"Perhaps I'd better stop here so none of your neighbors will see you getting out of a strange car," said Mrs. Graymalkin.

"Swell idea!" agreed Kerby. "I sure hope Mrs. Pembroke isn't home yet!"

Mrs. Graymalkin's car squeaked to a sudden stop. "Hurry, boys! There's no time for long good-byes!" she cried.

The boys raced for home, not even stopping to watch as the old car disappeared down the street. Their eyes were turned straight ahead. And then suddenly Fenton cried, "Look! There's a car parked in front of Mrs. Pembroke's! Her lights are on! She's back!"

They raced up the front lawn, crept alongside the hedge between the houses, and saw Mrs. Pembroke through the basement window.

"Xerxes! Stop hiding and come here this minute! Xerxes!" she said.

They fell back in the darkness on their side of the hedge because Mrs. Pembroke was staring straight at them. Then they realized she was looking at the open window.

"Oh, that bad cat!"

Upstairs in the living room, they could see three other women settled at the card table, waiting for Mrs. Pembroke. Meanwhile, she was starting up the basement stairs.

Outside in Waldo's pen, Xerxes was whining and barking.

"Come on, Fenton. Let's get inside my house before she comes out so we can make Waldo shut up if he starts meowing."

They raced up the back steps, and Kerby closed the door quietly just as Mrs. Pembroke opened hers.

"Meow?"

"Quiet!" snapped Kerby, grabbing Waldo.

"Here, Xerxes! Come, baby!" called Mrs. Pembroke from her top step.

Kerby groaned. "If she stands there long enough looking around, she'll see there's something barking in the pen that isn't Waldo!"

Cool as ever, Fenton had been thinking. "What's her telephone number?" he asked.

"What?"

"Call her. Make her go inside to answer the phone. We've got to get Xerxes out of sight!"

Kerby ran to the kitchen and called the number as fast as he could.

"Hurry, Kerby! She's looking over this way!"

As he stood waiting, Kerby could see one of the women next door answer the telephone.

"Hello?" she said in his ear.

"Er—hello? May I speak to Mrs. Pembroke?"

"Mrs. Pembroke? Why, yes. Just a moment, she's outside. I'll call her."

He saw the woman leave the room. From outside he could hear Mrs. Pembroke say, "What? The phone? Who is it?"

Grumbling, she went inside. Her back door had hardly closed when Kerby's opened, and Fenton shot down the back steps.

Kerby had laid the receiver on the table, but he
could hear Mrs. Pembroke saying, "Hello?"

Fenton came charging in, carrying Xerxes like a
football. Fenton glanced around and asked,
"Where's Waldo?"

"I put him in the basement," said Kerby.

"Swell!"

"Hold Xerxes, and I'll go mix the stuff."

All the way from next door they could still hear
Mrs. Pembroke shouting, "Hello? Hel-lo!"

"And hang up the phone," added Kerby as he went down to the basement, carefully closing the door behind him. The important thing now was to keep Waldo and Xerxes apart until the right moment.

Waldo kept meowing and rubbing against Kerby's legs while Xerxes continued whining and barking upstairs. How Kerby ever managed to mix the liquid under such conditions was past understanding!

When he had finished, he wasted no time.

"Hold still," he ordered, grabbing Waldo's bushy tail and pouring the liquid all over it. Then Kerby grabbed the dog by the collar and led him quickly upstairs.

"Make way! Here I come with Waldo," called Kerby. "We'll do this outside. I'll go out the front door so Mrs. Pembroke won't see us."

"OK, come ahead," called Fenton, slipping into the dining room with Xerxes. "I'll be right behind you."

Hurrying into the side yard, Kerby held tightly to Waldo as Fenton appeared, carrying Xerxes.

"Meow!" whined Waldo.

Too late Kerby made a grab to quiet him.

"Xerxes!" called Mrs. Pembroke from her backyard. She had come outside again. They heard her say to one of her friends, "I hear Xerxes over in the Maxwells' yard! I'll bet that dog of theirs has scared him again. I'm going over and bring the poor baby home!"

Kerby froze in his tracks. Mrs. Pembroke was coming. She was on her way. If the mixture didn't work, if something didn't happen at once, they were done for. They would never be able to explain what had been going on. Nobody would believe them. They might end up in jail for the rest of their days!

Fenton dropped Xerxes on the ground. The big cat barked delightedly and rushed up to Waldo, ready to play.

Xerxes sniffed once. Leaping straight for Waldo's tail, drawn to it by the mysterious mixture, the cat took what was meant to be a playful bite.

"R-r-row-w!"

When Xerxes finally hit the ground, he was a scared cat racing for home. When Waldo came down, he was a howling dog right behind the cat. Mrs. Pembroke turned the corner just in time for both of them to zoom between her legs. She was so surprised that she didn't see two small figures dive into the bushes near the front of the house.

Hot Dogs for Waldo

Waldo frowned at the bandage on his tail.

"Well, it was your own fault," said Kerby. "But don't worry, we'll take the bandage off before anyone sees it."

Waldo sniffed. His feelings hurt more than his tail.

"Of course, Mrs. Pembroke will yell about how you chased Xerxes again, but we know you had a right to do that. After all, he was in our yard."

As soon as Waldo quieted down, the boys would have their cookout. They figured a few hot dogs would make a new dog out of Waldo.

Suddenly Fenton grinned. "I suppose your folks will tell us about the swell time they had."

"Grown-ups!" said Kerby, shaking his head. "They don't know what a swell time is, do they?"

GLOSSARY

The glossary can help you find out the pronunciations and meanings of some of the words used in this book.

The pronunciation is shown after the word in this way: **ac cept** (ak sept'). The letters and signs are pronounced as shown in the pronunciation key. This key will help you to pronounce the words that are in the glossary.

FULL PRONUNCIATION KEY*

a	hat, cap	j	jam, enjoy	u	cup, butter
ā	age, face	k	kind, seek	ů	full, put
ä	father, far	l	land, coal	ü	rule, move
b	bad, rob	m	me, am	v	very, save
ch	child, much	n	no, in	w	will, woman
d	did, red	ng	long, bring	y	young, yet
e	let, best	o	hot, rock	z	zero, breeze
ē	equal, be	ō	open, go	zh	measure, seizure
ėr	term, learn	ô	order, all		
f	fat, if	oi	oil, voice		
g	go, bag	ou	house, out		
h	he, how	p	paper, cup		
i	it, pin	r	run, try		
ī	ice, five	s	say, yes		
		sh	she, rush		
		t	tell, it		
		th	thin, both		
		ŦH	then, smooth		

ə represents:
a in about
e in taken
i in pencil
o in lemon
u in circus

A a

ac cept (ak sept'), **1** to take what is given or offered. **2** to receive with favor.

al ley (al' ē), a narrow back street in a town or city.

am ne sia (am nē' zhə), the loss of memory due usually to shock, illness, or brain injury.

at tic (at' ik), the part of a building just below the roof and above the other rooms.

B b

bar ter (bär' tər), to trade or exchange goods for other goods.

base ment (bās' mənt), the part of a building that is wholly or partly below the ground.

be ware (bi wer' *or* bi war'), to be careful; to be on guard.

brooch (brōch *or* brüch), a fancy pin that is usually fastened with a clasp.

buoy (boi), a floating object kept in a certain place on the water to warn against shallow water or hidden rocks.

bur ro (bėr' ō), a small donkey.

C c

calf (kaf), **1** a young bull or cow. **2** the young of several other large animals.

ca noe (kə nü'), a light boat moved with a paddle.

cap i tal (kap' ə təl), the city where the government of a state or country is located.

carve (kärv), to cut; to make by cutting.

charm ing (chär' ming), pleasing or delightful.

cheat (chēt), to trick; to play or to work in a dishonest way.

chip (chip), a small piece cut from wood or broken from china or stone.

clog (klog), a shoe that has a thick, wooden sole.

copy (kop′ ē), something that is made to be exactly like another; something made from the model of another.

cu ra tor (kyu̇ rā′ tər), one who is in charge of a museum, zoo, or other public place.

D d

dam age (dam′ ij), to harm so as to lessen usefulness or value.

de feat (di fēt′), to gain victory over; to overcome.

de fend (di fend′), **1** to protect or to keep safe. **2** to speak or to act in favor of.

dol phin (dol′ fən), any of the small whales that has a beaklike snout.

drach ma (drak′ mə), a Greek silver coin.

E e

e rupt (i rupt′), to burst forth.

ex act (eg zakt′), without a mistake; correct.

ex claim (ek sklām′), to call or to cry out; to speak suddenly with strong feeling.

F f

faint (fānt), weak; not clear.

fa vor (fā′ vər), kindness; goodwill.

file (fīl), a row of things or persons, one behind the other.

flute (flüt), a long, pipelike musical instrument.

for tune (fôr′ chən), **1** wealth; riches. **2** success; good luck.

G g

gain (gān), **1** to advance. **2** to arrive at.

gear (gir), a wheel that has teeth which fit into the teeth of another wheel.

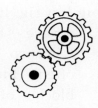

glance (glans), **1** to look quickly. **2** a quick look.

hat, āge, fär; let, ēqual, tėrm; it, īce; hot, ōpen, ôrder; oil, out; cup, pu̇t, rüle; ch, child; ng, long; sh, she; th, thin; TH, then; zh, measure; ə represents *a* in about, *e* in taken, *i* in pencil, *o* in lemon, *u* in circus.

grate ful (grāt' fəl),   feeling thankful because of a favor received.

grove (grōv), a group of fruit or nut trees standing together.

H h

ham mock (ham' ək), a hanging bed or couch.

har mon i ca (här mon' ə kə), a small wind instrument with metal reeds that is played by the mouth.

heap (hēp), a pile of things thrown or lying together.

her o (hir' ō),   any   person praised and admired for great deeds or qualities.

I i

ig loo (ig' lü),   a dome-shaped Eskimo   hut, often   built   of blocks   of   snow and ice.

i mag ine (i maj' ən), to form a picture of in one's mind; to have an idea.

in stant (in' stənt), **1** a moment of time. **2** immediate.

in stru ment (in' strə mənt), **1** a tool. **2** a device used to produce music.

in tend (in tend'),   to   have   a purpose in mind; to plan.

J j

jazz (jaz), a type of music in which   the   accents   fall   at unusual places.

jew el (jü' əl),   **1**   a   precious gem. **2** someone or something that is very special.

K k

ki mo no (kə mō' nə),   a   loose robe with wide sleeves and a broad sash worn in Japan.

L l

lad (lad), a boy; a young man.

lan guage (lang' gwij),   the speech of a particular race or nation.

la va (lä' və), the melted rock which flows from a volcano.

loom (lüm), a machine that is used for weaving cloth.

lum ber jack (lum' bər jak'), a person whose job is to cut down trees and to get out the logs.

M m

mare (mer *or* mar), a female donkey or horse.

mend (mend), to fix or to repair.

mer ry (mer' ē), gay; happy.

mis chief (mis' chif), a behavior that causes harm or trouble, often without meaning it.

mu se um (myü zē' əm), a building where objects of value and lasting interest are displayed.

O o

o bey (ō bā'), to do what one has been told to do.

odd (od), strange; queer.

oys ter (oi' stər), a mollusk that has a rough, irregular shell in two halves.

P p

pad dle (pad' l), an oar with a flat blade used to move and steer a small boat.

pas sen ger (pas' n jər), a person who travels on a bus, boat, train, or airplane.

pier (pir), a structure built out over the water and used as a landing place.

pig eon (pij' ən), a bird with a stout body and short legs.

pit y (pit' ē), to feel sorrow for another.

pro duce (prə düs' *or* prə dyüs'), to make.

prod uct (prod' əkt), that which is the result of work.

Q q

quay (kē), a solid landing place beside water, for ease in loading and unloading ships.

---

hat, āge, fär; let, ēqual, tėrm; it, īce; hot, ōpen, ôrder; oil, out; cup, pùt, rüle; ch, child; ng, long; sh, she; th, thin; TH, then; zh, measure; ə represents *a* in about, *e* in taken, *i* in pencil, *o* in lemon, *u* in circus.

R r

rein deer (rān' dir'), any of several deer having antlers and living in northern regions.

rel a tive (rel' ə tiv), a member of one's family.

re spon si bil i ty (ri spon' sə bil' ə tē), an obligation; being expected to account for.

rum ble (rum' bəl), a low, heavy, continuous sound.

S s

sa rong (sə rông'), a loose skirt made from a long strip of cloth, wrapped around the body.

serv ice (sėr' vis), a helpful act; being of aid to others.

shark (shärk), a large fish that eats other fish and may attack people.

speech less (spēch' lis), unable to talk.

sprin kle (spring' kəl), to scatter in drops or little bits.

sur vey (sər vā' *for 1*; sėr' vā *for 2*), **1** to measure the land for size, shape, or boundaries. **2** the plan or description of such a measurement.

T t

tai lor (tā' lər), someone who makes, alters, or repairs clothes.

tame (tām), taken from the wild state and made gentle.

tank (tangk), a large container for storing or transporting a liquid or a gas.

tour ist (túr' ist), one who travels for pleasure.

tow (tō), to pull or to tug by rope or chain.

trum pet (trum' pit), a musical instrument that has a curved metal tube ending in a bell.

twist (twist), to turn with a winding motion.

U u

u su al (yü' zhü əl), ordinary; normal; in common use.

V v

val u a ble (val' yü ə bəl), worth a great amount.

vet er i nar i an (vet' ər ə ner' ē ən), a doctor who treats injuries or diseases of animals.

view (vyü), **1** to see or to look at. **2** a scene.

vol ca no (vol kā' nō), an opening in the earth's crust from which steam, ashes, and lava are forced.

wal rus (wôl' rəs), a large sea animal related to the seal but having long tusks.

wax (waks), a yellow substance made by bees and used by them for building their honeycomb.

wear y (wir' ē), tired; worn out.

whine (hwīn), a high-pitched, complaining sound.

W w

wail (wāl), a long cry expressing pain or grief.

Y y

yarn (yärn), a thread used in weaving and knitting.

hat, āge, fär; let, ēqual, térm; it, īce; hot, ōpen, ôrder; oil, out; cup, put, rüle; ch, child; ng, long; sh, she; th, thin; TH, then; zh, measure; ə represents *a* in about, *e* in taken, *i* in pencil, *o* in lemon, *u* in circus.

(Acknowledgments continued from page 2.)

Farrar, Straus & Giroux, Inc. for the poem "Dream Song." Reprinted with the permission of Farrar, Straus & Giroux, Inc. from IN THE TRAIL OF THE WIND, edited by John Bierhorst, Copyright © 1971 by John Bierhorst.

Four Winds Press for "Scat!" Adapted from SCAT! by Arnold Dobrin. © 1971 by Arnold Dobrin. Adapted and reprinted by permission of Four Winds Press, a division of Scholastic Magazines, Inc.; and for "What Can It Be?" and "A Pair of Problems." From THE NONSENSE BOOK by Duncan Emrich, copyright © 1970 by Duncan Emrich. Reprinted by permission of Four Winds Press, a division of Scholastic Magazines, Inc.

Garrard Publishing Company for "Benjamin Banneker, the Builder." Copyright 1971 by Margaret Goff Clark. From "Benjamin Banneker" by Margaret Goff Clark, reprinted with the permission of Garrard Publishing Company, Champaign, Illinois.

(Acknowledgments continued on page 312.)

(Acknowledgments continued from page 311.)

Heritage Press for "Adventures of Paul Bunyan." Adapted from the book THE WONDERFUL ADVENTURES OF PAUL BUNYAN, retold by Louis Untermeyer. Copyright © 1945.

Holt, Rinehart and Winston, Inc. for the poem "Stopping by Woods on a Snowy Evening." From THE POETRY OF ROBERT FROST edited by Edward Connery Lathem. Copyright 1923, © 1969 by Holt, Rinehart and Winston, Inc. Copyright 1951 by Robert Frost. Reprinted by permission of Holt, Rinehart and Winston, Inc.

Alfred A. Knopf, Inc. for "Surprise in a Cornfield" and "The Buried City." Adapted by permission of Alfred A. Knopf, Inc., from VOLCANOES AND EARTHQUAKES, by Robert Irving. Copyright © 1962 by Irving Adler; and for "Beware the Man Without a Beard." Adapted by permission of Alfred A. Knopf, Inc., from BEWARE THE MAN WITHOUT A BEARD AND OTHER GREEK FOLK TALES, retold by Rose Neufeld. Copyright © 1969 by Rose Neufeld.

J. B. Lippincott Company and Harold Ober Associates Incorporated for the poem "There Isn't Time!" Copyright 1933, © renewed 1961 by Eleanor Farjeon. From POEMS FOR CHILDREN by Eleanor Farjeon. Copyright 1951 by Eleanor Farjeon. Reprinted by permission of J. B. Lippincott Company and Harold Ober Associates Incorporated.

Little, Brown and Company for "The Turnabout Trick." From THE TURNABOUT TRICK by Scott Corbett, by permission of Little, Brown and Co. in association with The Atlantic Monthly Press. Copyright © 1967 by Scott Corbett.

Lyons & Carnahan, Inc. for "Call Me Pilar." Adapted from "My Name is Miguel" from THE ALMOST GHOST AND OTHER STORIES by Leo C. Fay. Copyright © 1966 by Lyons and Carnahan, Inc.

McGraw-Hill Book Company for "The Tsar's Riddles." Adapted from THE TSAR'S RIDDLES, or The Wise Little Girl by Guy Daniels (translator). Copyright © 1967 by Guy Daniels and Paul Galdone. Used with permission of McGraw-Hill Book Company.

G. P. Putnam's Sons for "Kumi and the Pearl." Adaptation by permission of G. P. Putnam's Sons from KUMI AND THE PEARL by Patricia Miles Martin. Copyright © 1968 by Patricia Miles Martin.

Rand McNally and Company for "Bertram and His Giraffe." Adapted from the book BERTRAM AND HIS FUNNY ANIMALS by Paul T. Gilbert. Copyright © 1934.

Review Publishing Company for "Igloos Are for Tourists." Adapted from "Igloos Are for Tourists" by Margaret Primm Richter in CHILD LIFE Magazine. Copyright © 1970 by Review Publishing Co., Inc. (now The Saturday Evening Post Company).

Pauline Rothrauff for "Penny's Good Fortune." Adapted from "Penny's Good Fortune." Copyright © 1973. Published originally in WEE WISDOM magazine.

Charles Scribner's Sons for "Josefina February." Adapted from JOSEFINA FEBRUARY by Evaline Ness with the permission of Charles Scribner's Sons. Copyright © 1963 Evaline Ness.

"Sky Country" was based on an original legend which was first recorded by Dr. John R. Swanton in Bulletin 39 of the Bureau of American Ethnology, TLINGET MYTHS AND TEXTS (Washington, D. C.: Government Printing Office, 1909).

Sterling Publishing Company, Inc. for "The Playful Dolphin." Taken from the book "The Dolphin: Cousin to Man" by Robert Stenuit, © 1968 by Robert Stenuit, published by arrangement with Sterling Publishing Co., Inc., New York, N. Y. 10016.

Charles E. Tuttle Company, Inc. for "The Storm." Adapted from KO OF MENEHUNELAND by Gene and Connie Erger. Copyright © 1963 by Charles E. Tuttle Company, Inc., publishers, and used with their permission.

The Viking Press, Inc. for "Sugar on Snow." Adapted from SUGAR ON SNOW by Nancy Dingman Watson. Copyright © 1964 by Nancy Dingman Watson. Reprinted by permission of The Viking Press, Inc.; and for the poem "Two Witches" by Alexander Resnikoff from OH, HOW SILLY!, poems collected by William Cole. Copyright © 1970 by Alexander Resnikoff. Reprinted by permission of Joan Resnikoff.